HowExpert Presents

Kickboxing 101

A Beginner's Guide To Kickboxing For Self Defense, Fitness, and Fun

HowExpert with Nathan DeMetz

For more tips related to this topic, visit HowExpert.com/kickboxing.

Recommended Resources

- HowExpert.com – Quick 'How To' Guides on All Topics from A to Z by Everyday Experts.
- HowExpert.com/free – Free HowExpert Email Newsletter.
- HowExpert.com/books – HowExpert Books
- HowExpert.com/courses – HowExpert Courses
- HowExpert.com/clothing – HowExpert Clothing
- HowExpert.com/membership – HowExpert Membership Site
- HowExpert.com/affiliates – HowExpert Affiliate Program
- HowExpert.com/writers – Write About Your #1 Passion/Knowledge/Expertise & Become a HowExpert Author.
- HowExpert.com/resources – Additional HowExpert Recommended Resources
- YouTube.com/HowExpert – Subscribe to HowExpert YouTube.
- Instagram.com/HowExpert – Follow HowExpert on Instagram.
- Facebook.com/HowExpert – Follow HowExpert on Facebook.

Table of Contents

Introduction

What Is Kickboxing?

Kickboxing is a stand-up form of striking. It consists
of a variety of attacks, but is commonly known for
strikes with the hands and legs (punches and kicks).
This is only a small part of kickboxing, however, as the
form of combat includes knee strikes, elbow strikes,
open palm techniques, and many other stand-up
attacks.

Many people, maybe even you, envision kickboxing as
the atypical straight punches (the jab and cross) as
well as the atypical roundhouse kick, which is more
often simply referred to as a round kick. This is a
beginning point for kickboxing, but even a straight
punch or a round kick are not as simple as they first
seem. For example, there are different versions of the
round kick, or roundhouse kick. A round kick in Tae
Kwon Do is different from a round kick in Muay Thai.
The same can be said for other striking forms of
martial arts as well.

Kickboxing is a well-rounded form of martial arts that
is not in itself a traditional martial art. Kickboxing, as
I know it, is a culmination of many striking martial
arts. Depending on where a person has trained, and
with whom, the styles they are associated with may
differ. For me, I primarily use Boxing and Muay Thai,
while incorporating some techniques from other arts.
For an associate of mine, their base is in Tae Kwon Do
with supplemental training in boxing and Muay Thai.

The more you search and talk with different people or groups, the more you will see variety in what "kickboxing" is for each person.

The History of The Art

Just as kickboxing is diverse and hard to define in simple terms, so is the history of the art. Various forms of stand-up striking martial arts date back to ancient times. You can be sure that some forms, if we were able to truly follow them all the way back in time, predate historical records.

Muay Thai predates the 19th century and originates in Thailand. The style is the successor of Muay Boran. Other variations of Muay Thai and Muay Boran exist. Styles that predate Muay Boran and Muay Thai are argued to be basis for Muay Boran and other arts influenced, or are influenced by, Muay Boran.

Records on Karate vary depending on the style, historian, and other factors. According to some accounts, Karate can be traced back to Zen Buddhism in Western India with an inception date of around 1400 years ago. Others trace the history of karate back to the 19th century, but state possible earlier beginnings.

My point is, when you look at the details of and think about kickboxing, do not dial it down to one area or set of skills. Thinks of it as a larger spectrum of skills and disciplines that can be put to together in nearly infinite ways. Appreciate where the art has come from and where it will go.

What Will You Learn in This Manual?

The point of this manual is to impart on you as much of the basics as I can within the limited amount of space available. This will include proper stance, attacks, movement, and more. The idea is to provide you with a well-rounded, working knowledge that you can perfect on your own or with a partner, from home or in a class environment, as a primary learning tool or as a supplement to other learning. Specific chapters covered in this manual will be:

Chapter 1: Stance and movement: This chapter will cover the appropriate foot stance and hand positioning, as well as variations. Movement will also be covered and include lateral, side, and pivoting.

Chapter 2: Defense – blocking and evasion: This chapter will show you how to evade punches using traditional boxing movements, such as the slip or bob-n-weave.

Chapter 3: Attacking with punches: In this chapter, you will learn to attack with punches, such as the jab, cross, hook, and uppercut, as well as other variations.

Chapter 4: Basic elbow and knee attacks: Knees and elbows will be discussed in this chapter with multiple variations of both being covered. The round elbow, downward elbow, basic knee, and knee with head grab are some techniques you will learn.

Chapter 5: Basic kick attacks: Kicks of various types will be taught in this chapter. The kicks will be basic and include the rear-leg round kick, teep (push kick), and the front-leg round kick. Defensive maneuvers, such as the shielding and kick checking will be included as well.

Chapter 6: Putting it together: This chapter will show you how to put everything you learned together. It will outline potential combos and more.

Safety First

Before we move on, I want to emphasize the importance of safety. Safety is always an important issue to take into consideration. When performing martial arts, or any type of strenuous activity, injuries can occur. To minimize this, precautions should be taken. Always attempt to perform movement in a controlled manner. When working with a partner, be sure both of you understand what training will be covered. Decide what level of power and intensity will be used. Always practice in an area that is safe for training and use the necessary protective gear. This includes, but is not limited to, head gear, a mouth guard, gloves, and striking pads.

Chapter 1: Stance and Movement

Before learning any other aspect of kickboxing, you must first know how to stand and how to move. We will begin with stance. There are two basic stances for any type of striking based form of combat. They are the **Orthodox** and **Southpaw** stance.

The Orthodox stance is the positioning that a right-handed person generally uses. This puts their right hand, or power hand, and their right foot in the rear position. People who use the Southpaw stance are the exact opposite. Their left hand is in the rear position as is their left foot.

Stances can vary greatly in both the Southpaw and Orthodox stances. Foot positioning, knee bend, and other factors are aspects of stance. The following series of photos will outline some of the variations for foot positioning and knee bend in the Orthodox and Southpaw stances.

Orthodox Stance

Figure 1: This is the basic kickboxing stance that I use when throwing strikes. I suggest you use this same stance. It can vary slightly to accommodate your body type and to ensure comfort in movement. This stance is ideal for throwing quick and powerful strikes. I use a slightly deeper knee bend when I am evading certain strikes or throwing certain strikes. You will notice this as you work through the manual.

Figure 2: This is the basic stance that I use for movement. Having my feet more in line with each other allows me to push off the back foot in order to move forward. This same idea applies to other movement as well. I will go over movement further in this chapter.

Figure 3: This is an example of the deeper knee bend I will use.

Southpaw Stance

Figure 4: This is a foot shot of the southpaw stance. The stance is a reverse of the orthodox stance. It is used by a person who is left handed. The southpaw fighter has their left foot back and their right foot forward.

Figure 5: This is the southpaw stance with the deeper knee bend.

Figure 6: The southpaw stance with a slightly wider stance used for seating down on punches. This can be used in both the southpaw and orthodox stances. The wider stance can create greater power generation. This will be discussed more later.

Figure 7: In this image, the orthodox stance is displayed in full body view. The foot stance is slightly wider which is used for seating down on punches. This is more of a power stance than a movement stance. Notice that the hands are kept high and close to the face. Notice the slight bend in the knees.

Figure 8: This a left-side view of the stance form figure 7. Again, notice the slight knee bend, high and tight guard, and the slightly wider stance.

Figure 9: The right-side view of figure 7. From this angle, you can see how the head, elbows, knees, and body align. You can see the solidity of the foot stance.

The preceding stances referenced and imaged are the primary stances you will use in conjunction with this manual. There is one other stance you will also use called the side stance.

Side Stance

Figure 10: The side stance looks just how it sounds. You will stand with your body faced to the side with your head looking forward. The foot position is front to back, meaning one is in front of the other, standing on the same line.

Figure 11: The side stance works from both sides and is used for certain kicking strikes. A sidekick and a turning back kick (spinning back kick) are two kicks thrown from this position.

Figure 12: The side view of the side stance. Notice the positioning of the feet and the angle of the feet.

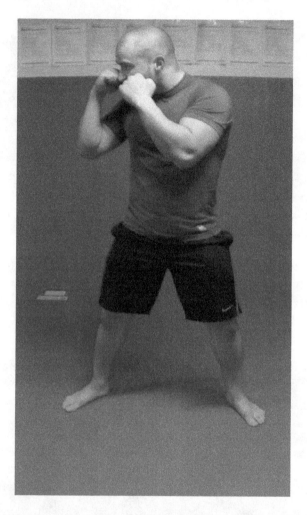

Figure 13: Full body view of the side stance. Your hands are still held high and the face looks forward toward your opponent.

Flat Footed vs. Ball Footing

In boxing and kickboxing, there are two basic types of footing. These refer to the way the bottoms of your feet contact the ground. The first is **standing flatfooted** while the second is **standing ball footed**. Standing flatfooted means standing with your entire foot touching the ground. This is the way most people stand every day and it is the way you want to stand when throwing certain strikes from the upper body.

Standing on the balls of your feet (ball footed) refers to standing with the heels of your feet slightly off the ground with your weight supported by the balls of your feet. The balls of your feet are the front part of the foot behind the toes. This footing is used for movement and for throwing certain strikes from the lower body.

Standing Ball Footed

Figure 14: It may be a little hard to see, but I am standing ball footed in this image. I am only slightly lifted. It does not need to be an extreme lift but rather just enough to distribute weight to the balls of the feet.

Figure 15: Here I am again standing ball footed although it is exaggerated. Being this

high on the balls of the feet when stationary is unnecessary. Only in mid-motion will you be elevated this high on the balls of the feet. At a standstill, this leads to an unbalanced stance.

Standing Flat Footed

Figure 16: Standing flatfooted means that you have the entire area on the bottom of your feet contacting the ground. This footing is good for establishing a solid base from which to throw punches. In this image, you will see I have the deeper knee bend I spoke of earlier. When throwing punches this knee bend helps me torque my body and throw more power into the punches. We will go over this in more detail further on.

Once you have the stance down, it becomes time to work on movement utilizing this stance. While walking is something people do every day, kickboxing movement is not. The two are fundamentally different, although the result is the same. Not only do the movements differ, but so do the intentions behind the movement. When walking you are only concerned with getting from one place to the next. In kickboxing, you will be concerned with getting from one place to next while avoiding strikes, or other attacks, and setting up strikes or counter strikes. This ability to move while evading or striking is an essential part of kickboxing.

When walking, you place one foot in front of the other to move forward. To move backward, you place one foot behind the other and move backward. When moving forward in a kickboxing stance, you will step forward with your front foot, then slide the back foot forward until you are in your original stance. When moving backward, you will step back with the rear foot then slide the front foot back until you are again in stance. That is the basic idea for movement in stance. The following images will outline movement in detail.

Forward Movement

Figure 17: You will be in forward with the stance for movement that I mentioned earlier in figure 2. This is ideal for movement as it allows the feet to flow in a line during movement. This creates smooth footwork and allows you to flow over the ground instead of the traditional walk. This is faster than a walk, but slower than a run. It allows you to maintain your stance. The front foot will slide forward in the direction of the arrow.

Figure 18: The front foot slides forward. You temporarily have a slightly wider stance from front to back. This is normal and you would not be able to move without some type of increase in stance width. The rear feet will slide forward next.

Figure 19: The rear foot slides forward. You have now effectively completed one step. Remember, you are not walking one foot in

front of the other. You are sliding the front foot forward then allowing the rear foot to slide forward behind it. This keeps you in your stance with your lead hand forward. Keep your hands high, head slightly tucked, and move on the balls of your feet. Repeat until you have covered the distance you need to move.

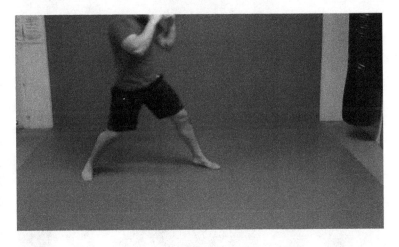

Figure 20: Move forward again. The front foot steps forward first, creating a temporarily larger stance width.

Figure 21: The rear foot then follows and closes the stance. Your lead hand is forward with your hand high and your head slightly tucked. Repeat this until you move the distance you need to achieve.

Figure 22: Front foot slides forward.

Figure 23: Rear foot slides.

Figure 24: Front foot slides forward.

Figure 25: Rear foot slides.

Backward Movement

Figure 26: Backward movement is achieved via the same mechanics as forward movement.

The only difference is that you slide with your back foot first.

Figure 27: Slide your back foot out while keeping your lead hand forward, hands high, and chin slightly tucked.

Figure 28: Follow with your front foot.

Figure 29: Slide your rear foot.

Figure 30: Follow with your front foot.

I realize that this likely sounds boring and tedious. Proper movement is essential to any martial art. Kickboxing is no different. If you take a boxing course, a Tae Kwon Do course, or even a jiu-jitsu course, the fundamentals of standing are going to incorporate proper stance and proper movement.

Do not look at this as a chore. Look at it as a foundation. With improved movement, evasion becomes easier and striking on the go becomes possible. With improved evasion, you take less damage. With increased striking ability, you do more damage. When it comes to kickboxing, or any striking sport, these are necessary abilities. If you don't want to do this, you might as well stop reading now.

I can understand the tediousness of this movement. Practicing moving isn't fun or exciting and it doesn't directly teach how to attack or defend against an opponent. To that end, I suggest incorporating movement work into your warm up and cool down. Every workout should start with a warm up and end with a cool down. I like to do my training sessions in rounds. After my treadmill work, I start with two to three, five-minute warm up rounds on the mat. I practice my footwork and shadow box. This is a great way for you to incorporate footwork (movement). The same can be said of the cool down. Set aside one to two rounds, or a specific time frame, and incorporate some footwork (movement) into it.

Diagonal Movement

Diagonal movement is a bit unique in that it can be done in four directions instead of two, like the front to back movement. Let me illustrate. Imagine that you are standing on the middle of the line in your stance facing the right side of the page. Forward movement would allow you to move to the right side of the page while rear movement would allow you to move to the left side of the page.

You

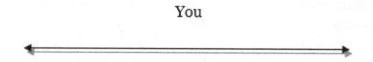

Now, imagine you are in the middle of the circle below and we are looking down at you from top view. The lines represent the diagonal directions you can move. There are four lines with two denoting rear movement and two denoting front movement.

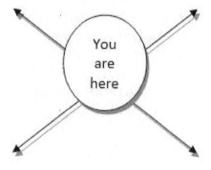

Ideally, diagonal movement does go in four directions, as illustrated by the previous images. However, in order to move forward or backward in one direction, you would need to change stances. This is something we do not want at this point. You should always maintain your stance. Again, let me illustrate, this time with a photo.

Figure 31: Diagonal movement is done is a forward diagonal or rear diagonal. We will start with rear diagonal movement. Notice the direction indicated by the arrow.

Figure 32: From your normal stance, you step backwards with your rear foot. As with the front to back movement you will be in a larger than normal stance for a moment. Remember to keep your hands high and your stance

facing forward. Keep your eye on your opponent.

Figure 33: You now slide the front foot back to finish the movement. This is one diagonal step backwards.

Figure 34: Forward diagonal movement is essentially the same as rear diagonal

movement. The only exception is that you are moving forward.

Figure 35: Step forward in a diagonal motion with the front foot. Your hands are high, stance is proper, and your eyes are on your opponent.

Figure 36: Bring the rear foot forward.

Figure 37: Step forward in a diagonal motion with the front foot. Your hands are high, stance is proper, and your eyes are on your opponent.

Figure 38: Bring the rear foot forward.

Now, I want to cover one more point with diagonal movement. We have only moved in two directions so far, but, as I mentioned, diagonal movement can technically move in four directions. However, for the time being, I do not want you to move in the other two. If an opponent moves in a manner that would require this time of diagonal movement, you will pivot. The reason for this is that the other diagonal movement causes you to either step forward with you rear leg or step backward with you front leg without moving the other leg first. This causes a change in stance. For now, you want to maintain your stance. Let me show you what I mean.

Figure 39: In order to move diagonally you would need to step forward with your back foot. This would cause you to change stance. In this case, the change is from an orthodox stance to a southpaw stance. While it might seem a simple change, standing in a different stance can be awkward until you get used to it. That takes practice. For now, pivot or side step if someone moves in a manner that would result in this type of diagonal movement from you.

Side to Side Movement

Side-to-side movemnt is performed just as it sounds. Using one leg, you step to the side you wish to move and immediately follow with the opposite leg. For a moment, your stance will be slightly wider and you will in a more forward stance. Once you bring the second leg across to finish the side step, your stance will again be normal. Allow me to illustrate.

Figure 40: This is your normal stance. It is staggered with your lead leg forward and your rear leg back. From here, you will initiate the side step with one leg or the other.

Figure 41: In this image, I side step with my lead leg by moving it to the outside of my body. This is how the side step should always start in this manner. There should be no crossing of the legs.

Figure 42: I now follow my front leg with my rear leg. This closes the wider than normal stance and put me back in my original stance.

Figure 43: I now step to the right by moving my back leg in the direction that I want to move.

Figure 44: I follow my rear leg with my front leg. I have now completed the side step.

Figure 45: The motion for the side step is the same regardless of how many times it is done. Always start the side step with the leg closest to the direction you want to move...

Figure 46: step with that leg first...

Figure 47: then follow with the other leg.

Pivoting

Pivoting is performed by rotating (pivoting) on one foot. This pivot can occur on the front or the rear foot, although it generally occurs on the front foot. The next series of photos will outline how to pivot on the front foot. Pivoting on the rear foot is essentially the same.

Figure 48: In this image, I am standing in an orthodox stance. Position yourself in the same way. You are going to pivot to face your right side. This will cause your rear foot to pivot toward your left side.

Figure 49: This image shows me in mid-pivot. Notice my rear foot is slightly off the ground as it is the foot moving. I am balancing on the ball of my front foot to facilitate the pivot. If

you stand flat-footed, the pivot is difficult and you could tweak (sprain) your ankle.

Figure 50: I have completed the pivot. Notice that I am still on the balls of my feet (it is a bit exaggerated for effect). This is to facilitate continued movement. If I wanted to throw punches, I would seat back on my feet for a flat-footed power stance.

Figure 51: Now I will show you how to pivot to the other direction. You will start from the original stance. Notice in the image I am again in my standard stance facing forward. From here, I will pivot (rotate) to face my left side. My rear foot will pivot to my right.

Figure 52: You pivot in the same manner as the first pivot. It is that simple. Pivoting is an easy move to perform but it can take practice to become fluid with it.

Chapter Review

In this chapter, we have reviewed how you should stand (stance) and how you should move (movement) when practicing kickboxing. Understanding these principles are essential to kickboxing. You should have a working knowledge of them as you proceed forward.

Practice Suggestions

- Practice each set of movements individually first. Practice moving forward for a set number of repetitions or for time before moving to the next movement.
- Use a predetermined rep range or time frame. 5, 10, 15, or 20 steps in one direction is a good place to start. For example, do ten forward steps in one direction, pivot, then do ten steps forward again. If you prefer time, try using intervals of 15 seconds such as 15, 30, 45, etc.
- Once you are comfortable with movement in one direction, move in two directions, then three, and so on. For example, step forward ten steps and then backward ten steps. Once you are comfortable with that, add in ten side steps in each direction.

Chapter 2: Defense – Blocking Punches and Evasion

Defense is essential to surviving a fight. While being able to attack will incapacitate an opponent, proper defense will keep you from being incapacitated. Imagine for second a man running into a fight with his hands down and trying to swing punches from the waist. This man is leaving his head wide open for a punch and runs the risk of being knocked out.

Now let's imagine his opponent. This man has his hands high and easily blocks the telegraphed punches thrown from the first man's waist. The second man in turn capitalizes on the first man's exposed head and punches him in the face, knocking him out. This is a very real scenario and one you want to avoid.

Defense encompasses blocking and evasion. Both aspects are equally important. Blocking allows you to defend against a strike and prevent it from doing damage to important tissue, such as allowing a hook to hit the arm instead of the head. Evasion prevents the punch from ever landing and this is the ideal scenario.

The Rock Back

Figure 53: The rock back is my favorite evasive maneuver. It allows me to stay in the pocket and not get hit. It can be used to avoid any type of head punch. The best part about it is that it is simple to learn and perform. The rock back simple requires that you lean back. To perform the move, you start in your normal stance.

Figure 54: You then just lean back at the waist. Be sure to keep your hands high. Unless your opponent is right on top of you, their punch will miss in this position. Remember, like all moves, this has to be applied with proper timing. If it is not, you likely will get punched in the face.

Figure 55: Return to the start position. Remember to always keep your hands high to protect your face.

Slipping

Slipping is one of the best-known evasive maneuvers in boxing. It is used to avoid straight punches, the jab, and the cross. Slipping is performed by moving your body to the outside of the attacker's punching arm as the punch is thrown. Like all moves, this must be applied with proper timing to be effective. This is effective for boxing environments as well as kickboxing or MMA environments. The following images will illustrate. This is my second favorite evasive maneuver.

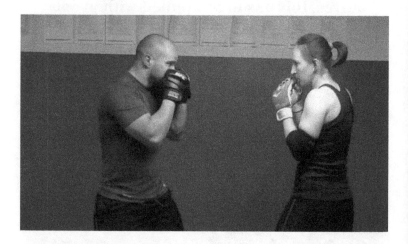

Figure 56: In this image, my partner and I are squared up. We are "in the pocket" and ready to bang (not really but for illustrative purposes). From this position, the slip is performed to avoid a punch.

Figure 57: I throw a jab toward my partner. She leans to the side slightly to avoid the punch. Notice that she is NOT doing a dramatic lean to the side. There is no need for this. You should move only the minimal amount needed to avoid the punch. This allows you to react quickly and efficiently. The less distance you move, the quicker you can return to the start position. A good rule of thumbs is to move six to eight inches to the side.

Figure 58: Return to start position.

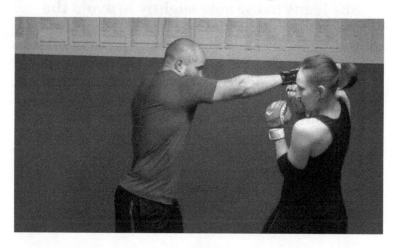

Figure 59: I now throw the cross. My partner leans to the outside of the punch. Remember, always move to the outside of the punch. If you slip to the inside, you could move into a second punch.

Figure 60: Return to start position.

Figure 61: Here is a rear view of my partner slipping the jab. Notice that she has not done some dramatic lean, but rather moved roughly six to eight inches to the outside of the punch. This has allowed her to avoid the punch.

Figure 62: My partner does the same thing here with the cross. In both of these images, she has plenty of space between her and the punch. She could have slipped even less, especially with the cross but this is effective.

Bob-N-Weave

The Bob-N-Weave is a boxing staple. It is not as common in kickboxing or MMA due to the potential for knee strike. In kickboxing, a person performing the Bob-N-Weave leaves themselves open to a knee to the face at the bottom of the movement. However, in a boxing oriented setting this move is efficient. I am not a big fan of the move due to the timing required to effectively perform it and the potential for a knee strike. The rock back is a much better alternative. When possible, use the rock back move instead of the Bob-N-Weave. However, there are many people who use this move with success, so it is essential to learn.

Figure 63: The Bob-N-Weave starts in the basic stance. In this image, I am again the attacker and my partner is the defender. The move is used to evade a hook shot.

Figure 64: I throw a right hook. The defender ducks under the hook in a "U" shaped manner moving from right to left. In this image, she

has begun her descent as my punch is approaching her.

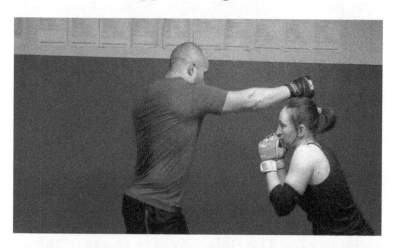

Figure 65: The defender continues her "U" motion, which causes her to travel under my punch as it moves. Again, she is moving right to left since my punch is moving toward her left side. Notice that the punch is just above her head. This is fine. The "U" does not have to be excessive.

Figure 66: The defender is now on the ascent part of the "U". My punch has now cleared her head and she is moving back to the start position.

Figure 67: The defender has returned to start position, as have I.

Head Movement (and Movement in General)

Head movement may be one of the most underrated defensive maneuvers. It is effective at avoiding punches, but also at disrupting an attacker's throwing pattern. A still target is easier to aim for, while a moving target means the striker has to move with the target to hit it. This can be enough to stifle an attacker's offense.

Head movement can also allow you to set up strikes and counter strikes easier. When throwing strikes there is always some kind of "tel" or form of telegraphing. Telegraphing is a movement before the strike is thrown. With punches, it is the movement of the shoulder before the punch is thrown. For a round kick, it is the turn of the hip before the kick is thrown.

When a person utilizes movement, in this case head movement, the tel is harder to see. This is because you are already in movement so, the attacking movement can be mistaken for general movement instead of striking movement. Some of the best strikers use head movement, or other types of movements such as feints, to confuse their opponent.

Head movement, and movement in general, is not confined to boxing, kickboxing of any one martial art, or form of combat. It is not even confined to stand up fighting. Ground fighting methods can benefit from movement as well. Again, let's look at the example of the still target vs. the moving target. If you are laying on the ground with a person in your **guard** (this is a jiu-jitsu term if you want to reference it) and a person is trying to hit you, you don't just want to lay there. You want to move either by **shrimping** (another jiu-jitsu term), obtaining wrist/arm control, or using some other defensive movement.

Movement is something I cannot stress enough. It is an essential part of defense and can keep you from getting hurt. Utilize movement as often as possible and look to perfect movements that work for you. Protect yourself, my friend.

Figure 68: Head movement is easy to perform, but it can be hard to implement in a fight. Head movement simply means moving the head and it starts from the basic stance (although it can be used in any position, see the previous paragraph). Head movement is actually a misleading term. The "head" movement actually occurs at the waist. You lean, bend, or twist at the waist to move the head from harm's way.

Figure 69: In this image, I have moved to the side. Essentially, I am slipping (see the slipping section). This movement can be used to confuse the opponent and make them throw a punch in the wrong direction.

Figure 70: Now I am leaning to the opposite side as if slipping. Again, this can be used to confuse the opponent. Conversely, I can also throw a punch from here. Potentially, my opponent thinks I am just moving for evasive purposes. If I throw an uppercut to the head or a hook the body, I might catch my opponent off guard.

Figure 71: In this image, I am ducking down as if to do the Bob-N-Weave. While the Bob-N-Weave is used to avoid hook punches, it can also be used as part of general head movement to confuse an opponent and avoid strikes. At any point in the movement, I can throw a punch should the opportunity arise. For this half-ducked position, I can throw a hook to the body or explode upwards to deliver a hook to an exposed jaw.

Figure 72: The same idea applies here. I am coming back up from the Bob-N-Weave. From here, I can throw a hook or a straight shot with my left hand. My body is already torqued in that direction and ready to spring. Keep this is mind as you practice head movement and try to incorporate strikes.

Chapter Review

In this chapter, we have reviewed how you avoid and defend against punches. Properly blocking punches, or avoiding them altogether prevents you from taking damage. This can make the difference between winning and losing a fight. Practice the included movements until they become second nature.

Practice Suggestions

- Practice each of the movements in the chapter until you have a feel for them.
- Practice with a partner whenever possible to make the movements more realistic.
- Try the movements in different orders to avoid getting stuck in a pattern and to help the moves become second nature.

Chapter 3: Attacking with Punches

Punching is striking at its most basic. Every person has, at one point or another, thrown a punch, whether in anger or in jest. At a glance, throwing a punch is a simple task. You just have to push your arm out. However, this does not make for a good punch. A proper punch follows a prescribed technique that maximizes form and speed to translate into power. That is what we will cover in this chapter.

There are only several different punches in striking: Jab, cross, front hook, rear hook, front uppercut, and rear uppercut. These are all the basic punches and other punches, such as the body shot, are just variations of these. Take notice that I referred to "front" and "rear" punches as opposed to left or right. I use this terminology because it is a universal language for both the orthodox and the southpaw stances. If you tell an orthodox person to throw a left, it will be a front shot. If you tell a southpaw person to throw a left, if will be a rear shot.

I say other punches are variations of these punches because, in essence, they are. A hook to the body is simply a variation of the hook. A jab to the body is a variation of the jab. It is that simple. The same idea applies to punches from the clinch, on the ground, and everything in between.

The Jab

The jab is the most basic punch in kickboxing and boxing. It is thrown off the lead hand. Notice that I say the lead hand and not the right or left hand. A person who stands in an orthodox position will have their left hand as their lead hand, while the Southpaw person will have their right hand as their lead hand. Due to this, I refer to the lead (front) and rear hands. That way the idea applies to both Orthodox and Southpaw stances.

Figure 73: This is the starting position for the jab.

Figure 74: Throw the jab straight out from the body. The punch is thrown quickly with a complete turnover of the hand. Notice how the back of my hand is facing skyward. My fist is closed and my knuckles are forward. The elbow should stay tight and not flair out excessively when this punch is thrown. If the elbow is flaring out, then correct it.

Figure 75: Return the punch to the start position. This should be a quick return. Do not leave your hand "hanging" in the air or allow it to return slowly. This exposes your face and leaves you vulnerable to a counter strike. Ideally, the punch should return as quickly as it was extended.

Figure 76: This is the front view of the jab.

Figure 77: Throw the punch.

Figure 78: Return to the start position.

The Cross

Figure 79: The jab is thrown in the same manner as the jab except with the rear hand. You will throw the punch straight out in a quick manner and return it just as quick.

Figure 80: Notice how my non-punching hand is protecting my face. Whenever you throw a punch with one hand, the other hand should be protecting the face. Notice how my punching had is completely turned over and my knuckles are forward.

Figure 81: Return to start position.

Figure 82: This is the front view of the cross.

Figure 83: Throw the punch straight out.

Figure 84: Return to start position.

The Hook

The hook is arguably the most powerful punch that can be thrown. The reason for this is that the body can be torqued in order to deliver more power. This is especially true with the rear hook. Due to the greater distance from target, the rear hook can gain more momentum and deliver more damage.

All punches use some form of hip drive and trunk rotation to deliver power. This is most applicable to the hook. Due to the turning nature of the hook, the hips and trunk are able to rotate which results in greater power output. This power is transferred into the target and can cause more damage when properly applied. Where the jab will generally cause damage through repetition, the hook can offer one-punch knockout power.

All punches require correct technique for optimal results. This is truer with the hook. The shoulder, elbow, wrist, hips, knees, and all need to rotate in proper alignment for maximum power. Without this technique, power is lost and a person can become unbalanced in the movement, which leaves them open to attacks. Let's look at the hook.

Figure 85: The hook starts from the standard stance.

Figure 86: To throw the front hook, twist your body slightly toward the front arm. This torques the punch.

Figure 87: Rotate explosively out of this torque. The punch will travel in a circular motion toward the face (jaw line) of the attacker. This image shows mid punch.

Figure 88: The punch stops once it has hit its target. If you miss, the elbow should not pass your face before returning your arm to the start position.

Figure 89: Return the punch to the start position. You can now throw the rear hook. It starts from the standard stance.

Figure 90: It travels in the exact same manner as the front hook. You will be able to achieve more rotation with the rear hook.

Hook to the Body

Figure 91: The front and rear hook can also be thrown to the body. The dynamics are generally the same. The main difference comes in the path that the punch travels.

Figure 92: There is a downward angle with the rear hook to the body...

Figure 93: before it returns to the start position. You can now throw the rear body shot...

Figure 94: which travels with the same downward trajectory. Return to the start position.

The Uppercut

Figure 95: The uppercut works in much the same manner as the hook.

Figure 96: You will torque your body toward the side of you front hand when throwing the front uppercut.

Figure 97: It will travel at an upward angle toward the head (instead of across like the hook)

Figure 98: The punch ends when connection to the target is achieved. If you miss, do not let the elbow pass your face.

Figure 99: Return to start position. You can now throw the rear uppercut.

Figure 100: It moves in the same manner as the front hook, except there will be more rotation (similar to the rear hook).

Figure 101: The front and rear uppercuts can also be thrown to the body. Similar to the hooks to the body, the uppercut to the body will simply travel a lower path. This shows the body uppercut.

Figure 102: A shot of the rear body uppercut.

The 1-2 and the #6 Combo

Once you have learned the basic punches as individual moves, you can start putting them together in combos. A combo is simply a series of strikes, in this case punches, thrown in succession. The **1-2 Combo** is the basic combo learned with punches. It is the jab followed by the cross. Here is an example:

Figure 103: The 1-2 Combos start for the basic stance.

Figure 104: Throw the jab.

Figure 105: As the jab is returning you throw the cross. Then you return both hands to the start position. It's essentially that simple, but will take practice to perfect.

The **#6** combo is a series of six punches chained together. It focuses on using the torque created from each punch to set up the next punch. For example, when you throw the jab, you torque the body so that it is primed to throw the cross. When you throw the front hook, you torque the body so that it is primed to throw the rear hook. Think of it as elastic buildup. When you throw one punch, the muscles on that side elongate while the muscles on the other side shorten. This shortening causes a buildup of energy that can be utilized.

Working with that principle in mind, you will now learn the **#6** combo. The combination consists of the following punch order:

1. Jab,
2. Cross,
3. Front hook,
4. Rear hook,
5. Front uppercut, and
6. Rear uppercut.

After the last punch is thrown, you reset to the start position with your hands high.

Figure 106: This is the start position for the #6 combo. It is your normal staggered stance.

Figure 107: You throw the jab. As you are pulling the jab back...

Figure 108: You throw the cross. As the cross is coming back...

Figure 109: you throw the front hook. As the front hook is coming back...

Figure 110: you throw the rear hook. As the rear hook is coming back...

Figure 111: yu throw the front uppercut. As the front uppercut is coming back...

Figure 112: you throw the rear uppercut.

Figure 113: Return to start position.

Chapter Review

In this chapter, you have learned how to throw the six basic punches that are used in boxing and kickboxing. These are the jab, cross, front hook, rear hook, front uppercut, and rear uppercut. Mastering these will be key to the boxing portion of kickboxing.

Practice Suggestions

- Start the learning process by practicing each punch individually. Then practice two together, then three, and so on.
- Use a predetermined rep range. 5, 10, 15, or 20 for learning the punches. For example, do 10 jabs followed by 10 crosses.

- Once you are comfortable with one punch, start comboing. Work up to the #6 combo. Try mixing up the combinations as you get more comfortable.

Chapter 4: Basic Elbow and Knee Attacks

Elbow and knees strikes are just as they sound. When performing an elbow strike you will hit the attacker with an elbow. When performing a knee strike, you will hit the attacker with a knee. When executed properly, elbow and knee strikes are the some of the most devastating strikes.

The elbow is devastating for a few reasons. The first is the rotating motion that occurs with most elbow movements, such as the round elbow. Similar to the hook, this adds body torque which increases the power of the elbow, albeit for less range than the hook. The second, and most devastating aspect of an elbow strike, is the contact made by the tip of the elbow. The tip, or point, of the elbow is sharp. Hitting an attacker with this point has a high likelihood of cutting the person open. Bone to soft skin can be terribly damaging.

The knee is devastating due to the hard kneecap combined with leg power. With few exceptions, the legs are the most powerful muscle group in the body. They can deliver more power per inch than a punch can. Put this power behind a hard object and the effect of a hit is magnified. A knee to can break ribs, crack an orbital socket, and knock a person out.

Figure 114: You are going to start with the basic round elbow. It is called the round elbow because it travels in half circle with a slightly upward trajectory. Start from your basic stance. When throwing an elbow, the hand should be open. Elbows can be thrown with a closed hand but the range of motion is limited and they are generally slower. Having the hand open allows you to tuck it close to your body.

Figure 115: This image shows the front elbow in mid-strike. Notice that the elbow follows an upward trajectory. It has to follow this upward trajectory to achieve the top position needed to strike the face cross ways.

Figure 116: Once the elbow has reached the necessary striking level, it travels straight across the opponent's face. The pointy part of the elbow should strike the opponent. Notice how the hand on my striking arm is tucked in close to my chest. This is where the hand should stop.

Figure 117: Return to start position. Repeat the same steps for the rear elbow. Like the rear hook, there will be more extension of the body. Refer to the rear hook for more details. You are now ready to throw the upward elbow.

Figure 118: The upward elbow can start from the hands high position but it will have less momentum. To add more momentum, drop

the elbow slightly before throwing. This will be a bit of a tel, but when done quickly enough the elbow will still successfully hit the target.

Figure 119: The upward elbow follows a straight trajectory moving skyward. You will strike the chin of the opponent.

Figure 120: This is the fully extended position for the upward elbow. Notice that you are in a

very exposed position on the striking side. You do not want to stay in this extended position for too long.

Figure 121: The next elbow you will learn is the downward elbow. The name is a bit misleading as the elbow actually comes downward with an inside angle. You will start from your standard stance.

Figure 122: The elbow first travels in an upward circle motion. See the arrow. This motion is necessary to get the elbow to the appropriate height to perform the strike.

Figure 123: Once the elbow has achieved the necessary height it begins its downward trajectory.

Figure 124: This image shows the elbow at the end of the strike. This attack is meant to come up and over the opponent's guard. It can be used to strike the opponent in the forehead, eye, or nose. This can lead to a broken nose, massive cut, or even a knockout blow. The blow follows the same path when thrown from the other side, again taking into consideration the greater range in motion.

Figure 125: Return to the start position. You are now ready to throw the upward angle elbow. It travels in much the same manner as an upward elbow except this time it has an angle to it, similar in nature to the downward elbow.

Figure 126: You will begin by dropping the elbow a few inches...

Figure 127: You will then begin driving it upward at an angle.

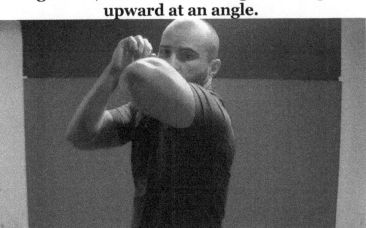

Figure 128: This is the top position for the elbow. You can extend a bit more than this but not too much. You expose yourself with this shot on both sides. You do not want to stay extended for long.

Figure 129: Return to start position.

Let's take a look at the following side shots for the elbows. As with the punches, you need to keep your hands high protecting yourself. Historically, when throwing elbows, a person would keep their non-striking hand open. Now this is a fine way to throw elbows. However, if you have been throwing punches then suddenly open your hands, a skilled opponent will be able to read that.

Now you might ask, how often am I going to run into a skilled opponent. Who knows? Maybe never. Maybe tomorrow. Why not train like everybody is skilled? The reason I say that is this, you never know what skill level a person has. Never underestimate anyone. They might surprise you.

Let me offer an example. I trained at a gym that offered a number of services including boxing and a weight training. Out in the weight training area I talked to a number of people. Over time I learned who was had combat knowledge and who didn't. At this gym, roughly 1 out of every 3 males had some form of combat knowledge. One out of three. With that in mind, let's train like everyone is skilled.

Keeping that thought in mind, let's look back at the elbows. Unless I am only training elbows, I like to keep my hands in fists. Punching is my primary weapon and so I want to stay with that hand positioning. With practice, I have become very adept at opening the striking hand right before I throw an elbow strike.

Figure 130: In this image, I am in my basic punching stance. My hands are tight to may face.

Figure 131: Right before I throw my elbow I allow my hand to open which facilitates the elbow strike. My non-striking hand is high to my face, in a fist.

Figure 132: In this image, I am using the open palm version of defense. This is fine when training elbows only but, when working with punches and elbows, try to keep the hands closed and high to the face. Open the striking hand right before an elbow strike.

Rear Elbows

Rear elbows are elbows thrown behind the body. In this manual, you are going to be shown three variations:

1. The elbow to the gut,
2. The elbow to the chin, and
3. The elbow to the side of the head.

Figure 133: The elbow to the gut is not a powerful elbow, but it can hurt. When properly placed this elbow will hit a person in the solar plexus (diaphragm) and cause the opponent to suck air. This can allow you to create space or set up a strike. It begins with a forward stance.

Figure 134: To perform this elbow you simply shove your elbow down and back in an arcing

or semi-circular motion. You then return it to the start position.

Figure 135: The next elbow is the rear elbow to the chin. It is delivered in much the same manner as the rear elbow to the gut. The difference lies in the range of motion and the need to lean forward slightly to facilitate full range of motion.

Figure 136: Start from a guard position. Drive your elbow down and back in an arcing or half-circle motion. As you do this, you will need to lean slightly forward. How far will be indicated by your height in comparison to the person you want to strike, and your flexibility. Stop the movement when you hit the person's jaw, or the imagined position of the person's jaw. Return to start position.

Figure 137: The next elbow is a round elbow to the side of the head. It travels in an upward round angle. Ideally, you will strike the opponent on the side of the head by the jaw or temple. Depending on exact distance from opponent and angle, it could vary. Start from the guard position. Your body will turn into the strike.

Figure 138: Your body will turn into the strike.

Knee Strikes

Knee strikes can be devastating attacks. The kneecap is a hard and relatively immobile surface. The legs are generally the strong muscle groups in the body. When the power of the leg is put against the kneecap it can result in a knockout, broken ribs, a broken nose, and many other injuries.

Figure 139: The forward knee strike is the most basic knee strike. This strike is done form a standard stance. In the image, my hands and arms are slightly more apart than normal. This is easier for me when throwing knees and kicks. The knee travels in a forward-upward angle.

Figure 140: This knee strike is often thrown from the clinch via head grab. You pull the

person's head down as you throw the knee upward. I am mimicking this in the image. This shot, when properly performed, is a knockout shot.

Figure 141: The forward knee can be thrown without the clinch as well. The motion will be basically the same as the previous version. The differences will be no head grab and a slight lean back.

Figure 142: Either knee can come with or without the clinch.

Figure 143: Attempt throwing both clinch and non-clinch version with both knees.

Chapter 5: Basic Kick Attacks and Defense

Attacking with kicks is an art unto itself. Every able-bodied person on Earth has the ability to perform a kick and has kicked something in their life. However, just because someone has kicked a ball or a heavy bag, it does not mean that the kick was done correctly. In kicking sports and martial arts that incorporate kicks, there is a specific technique with which to kick in order to achieve maximum efficiency.

In sports such as football or soccer, the kicker has to strike the ball with their foot using ideal technique to achieve maximum power, which turns into ball velocity. This same idea is applied to martial arts except this time the goal is maximum impact on a target. Speed and power are needed for both sports based kicking and martial arts based kicking. This does not mean that a larger, stronger person is going to be the more powerful kicker. To be a powerful kicker, this speed and power must be focused in proper technique. It is in this way that a smaller person can deliver a more powerful kick than a larger person.

Let me offer you an example of differences in power that are not based on size, but rather on years of technique practice. I have been using kick strikes for about three years now. A gentleman I know has been using kick strikes for close to thirteen years. He weighs around 140 pounds while I walk around at roughly 195 pounds. We both use the Bob heavy bag in our training. Bob weighs approximately 270 pounds with a full base. I have good technique so when I deliver a roundhouse kick I can almost knock Bob over. This other gentleman, the one that weighs roughly 140 pounds, can kick Bob over completely.

Now, do not let that example be intimidating to you. The gentleman I am referencing is a black belt in Tae Kwon Do and has trained Muay Thai in Thailand. He breathes martial arts. My point with that example is to stress the importance of correct technique. You should not expect to ever be perfect, let alone to be perfect quickly. With time and practice, you will become proficient in all the techniques exampled here, including the round kick. When I first started training Muay Thai, I could barely make a heavy bag move. With practice, I've become better.

The Teep

The teep is a type of front kick. It is also known as the foot-jab or push-kick. The kick is historically considered a defensive kick. It is used to push an opponent away from you. This can be used to set up other strikes as well. For example, you can push-kick an opponent from you to create distance and then deliver a round kick. The following series of images will illustrate the teep.

Figure 144: To complete the teep, you start by bringing the knee up. We will start with the back leg.

Figure 145: Bring the knee up to above waist height. You will lean slightly back while balancing on the non-kicking leg. From this position, you will kick straight out.

Figure 146: Kick your leg straight out. In this image, I am shadowboxing, but if faced with an opponent, I would target the gut area.

Figure 147: Your leg will come down as if finishing a forward step. You will be in a southpaw stance. Return to your normal stance.

Figure 148: This is the rear teep on the punching Bob dummy. This is the start position.

Figure 149: The leg is up high and ready to kick.

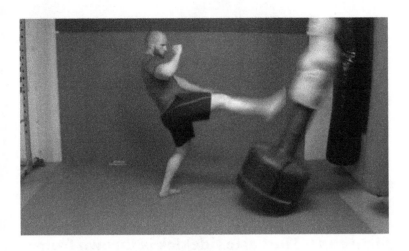

Figure 150: The extension of the kick.

Side Kick

The sidekick is essentially how it sounds. This kick is delivered from the side stance we reviewed earlier. The sidekick is an attacking kick that can be delivered to the legs, abdomen, and head. When properly applied this kick has serious power and can cause major damage to an opponent. For example, a sidekick delivered to the knee can snap the connective tissue supporting the knees and permanently handicap a person. The following is one variation of the side kick.

Figure 151: The basic sidekick is thrown from a side stance. This is the starting position. You will be throwing the kick with the back leg.

Figure 152: You start by bringing you rear leg forward and raising the knee. At the same time, you allow you non-kicking leg to rotate to facilitate the forward movement of the rear leg. The knee travels upward into the top

position for the side kick. Your hands stay high and protect the face as the leg is raised.

Figure 153: You then push the kick straight out from the body. You push from the hip of the kicking leg as well as the knee. You will have a lean back as you throw the kick. The rear hand stays high to the face and the front hand will drop down, as in the image.

The Basic Round Kick (Roundhouse Kick)

The basic round house kick is the staple of all kicking arts. It is the most commonly learned and executed kick across the board. Each style of martial arts, from karate to taekwondo, has its own variation of the round kick or roundhouse kick. In this guide, you will be shown what is commonly known as the Muay Thai style round kick.

Figure 154: The round kick begins in the basic stance. Your hands may be a little looser than the boxing hand placement. By this, I mean they can be a little further from the face to allow for the necessary arm movement that accommodates the kick. From here you will throw a rear leg round kick. It will travel in an upward arching motion.

Figure 155: You pivot on your non-kicking leg to facilitate the rotation needed for the kick. At the same time, you allow your body to turn and your leg to lift from the ground and travel in the arching motion. Your kicking side hand will drop down as a counter-balance. Your hand on the non-kicking side stays tight to the face for protection.

Figure 156: In this image, the kick is about to connect. Notice how my non-kicking foot is rotating at the ankle. Notice how may kicking side hand has dropped down. Notice that my far hand is tight by my face.

Figure 157: This is the completed kick. In this image, I have thrown a kick that would land at just above knee level of a person who is roughly 5"8" tall. Your kicking side hand does not need to be as far back as mine. I have exaggerated the movement slightly for effect.

Figure 158: Return to start position. The path the leg and body travels backwards is the same

as it traveled when performing the forward motion of the kick.

Figure 159: The round kick can be thrown to nearly any part of the body. This is of course dependent upon the striker's flexibility. An inflexible person will be limited in how high they can kick. In order to improve kicking height, improve flexibility along with technique. We are again at the start position for the round kick.

Figure 160: This time I have thrown the kick slightly higher. This kick would land on the mid to upper thigh of a person standing about 5"8". My shin would be placed solidly in the meat of their quadriceps (front of thigh). If you have never been kicked here, let me tell you that it hurts.

Figure 161: Return to the start position. Now you can throw a kick to the ribs of a person the same height as before.

Figure 162: Now I have landed a kick that would be at rib level. This can knock the wind out of someone and break ribs. Remember that you are pivoting on your non-kicking foot and allowing your body to turn. However, you should not lose sight of your target. Your foot will hit what you are looking at.

Figure 163: Return to the start position. You can now throw a kick to the neck/shoulder/head area. The path of the kick is the same.

Figure 164: Notice that my leg has more extension this time. As kick height increases, it becomes less possibly to keep the bend in the leg and strike with the shin. As you near the end of your leg reach, extend fully and

strike the with the instep (area where the foot and ankle meet).

Kicks on a Suitcase Pad

A suit case pad is a common training item used in kick oriented martial arts. It is designed to absorb the impact of kicks in an efficient manner and to allow the striker to kick in a natural manner. Kicks follow the same pattern as normal when using the suitcase pad.

When using the suitcase pad, always know how hard the kicks are going to be. The person in control of the action should determine the strength of the kicks. Traditionally the pad holder determines the strength of the kick. He or she will call out various kicks in a predetermined strength. Regardless of who controls the training, the pad holder should always know how hard the kicks will be. In this manner, they can brace themselves for the kicks and training is safer.

Figure 165: I set up for a round kick to knee level on the suitcase pad.

Figure 166: I throw the kick.

Figure 167: I reset and prepare to throw another kick.

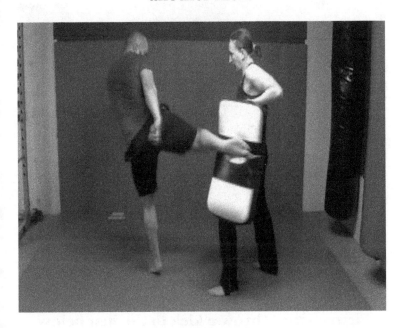

Figure 168: I throw a kick at about stomach level.

Figure 169: I reset again.

Figure 170: I throw a kick to the just below armpit level that would strike the ribs.

Figure 171: I reset again. You can practice like this with the suitcase pad. Single kicks, multiple kicks, front then rear, and other kicks can be thrown. Start simple and work up to advanced kicking.

The Front Round Kick

The front round kick can be accomplished in two ways. One is the switch kick. That will not be covered here. The other is a short round kick with the front leg in standard stance. This is just simply known as the front round kick. It does not have the power of the rear kick or the switch kick. However, with practice it can be thrown much quicker and can still have knockout capability.

Figure 172: This kick can be delivered from the standard stance. You can also widen your stance to deliver this kick. That is what I have

done in this image. The wider stance allows a bit more torque, which will result in a stronger kick.

Figure 173: To deliver this kick I am sliding my rear foot forward just a bit which will allow me to torque and lean back to deliver the kick. You can try it without moving the foot forward.

Figure 174: I pivot on my rear foot and begin the lean back. My kicking leg comes up and follows a small half-circle motion, similar to the rear round kick.

Figure 175: In this image, I have delivered a blow to the top of the thigh area.

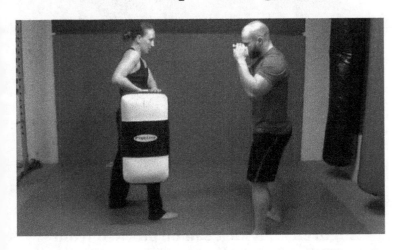

Figure 176: I return to start position.

Blocking Kicks

Blocking kicks, which is also referred to as checking kicks, is an essential defensive maneuver. More than punches, kicks hold damaging power. The power potential for the legs is far greater than that for the upper body. A person who takes too many kicks to the knee could find themselves with permanent knee damage. The same can be said for kicks to the thigh, or any other area for the matter.

When a person checks a low kick, they block the kick using their shin or the meat around the side of shin that make up part of the calf muscle. While taking the kick here will hurt, it will not hurt as bad as taking it on the knee or the thigh.

Figure 177: A kick can be blocked from essentially any stance.

Figure 178: For best protection, it is ideal to block at the top and the bottom. In this image, you can see I am protecting my head with my hand and have lifted my leg to block the low kick. The reason for blocking top and bottom is to avoid shots to both locations. Clever fighters will fake a few kicks to one area, setting the defender to block this area, then throw one to the unblocked area.

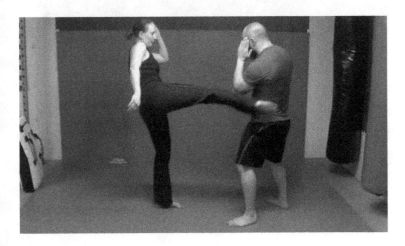

Figure 179: You can block singular areas. In this image, I am pulling my elbow to my side to defend against a rib strike.

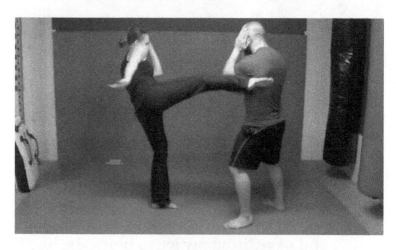

Figure 180: I use my elbow again here, this time to avoid a slightly higher kick.

Figure 181: Here, I am blocking with my elbow on the opposite side.

Figure 182: My partner in this image has not yet gained the flexibility to throw a high kick. However, she has thrown one to the shoulder and I am using a high block that would defend against a high kick.

Figure 183: In this image, I am blocking against a knee level strike. I am not shielding against a high kick, although my hands are high as they always should be.

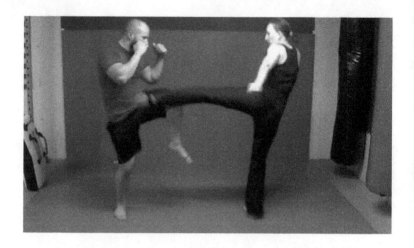

Figure 184: The same thing is happening here, except the opponent's kick would hit my stomach. Notice how I am using my knee in this image to block and in the last image I used the inside area of the shin/calf.

Chapter 6: Putting It Together

Once you have learned the individual moves you can start to chain together combos. You have already been introduced to some simple combos, the 1-2, and the #6 combo. You can build punch combos by working sections of the #6, mixing up punches, etc. The next series of images will show you how to mix punches with elbows and mix upper body strikes with lower body strikes. This will not be all inclusive of the number and pattern of combos available.

There are a finite number of combos available in martial arts standup striking. However, there are so many that the number may seem endless. This manual will cover but a few. Play around with combinations, experiment. The general rule of thumb is that combos should alternate sides. For example, you throw the jab in front of the cross. The reason for this is that the jab loads up the cross. The cross loads up the front hook and the front hook loads up the rear hook. Basically, when you throw a strike from one side you torque the other side and load up a shot from that side. Put combos together using this idea.

Now, combos can be thrown on the same side, but there is not wind up and this can take more skill. An example of a combo of the same side is the jab followed by the front hook. They both flow of the front hand. Now as mentioned this take more skill and practice. Start with alternating before moving on to same side strikes.

Another idea to follow is keeping it simple. I am all for fancy strikes and combos. I love Anthony Pettis style off the wall kicks and what not. That is actually a kick I have worked on for fun. However, being fancy may not be the best way to land strikes, especially outside of the ring where there are no rules. This is especially true if you are not as experienced with these moves. Anthony Pettis, and all other high-level fighters, have spent a great deal of time perfecting moves. With time, you can too, but in the beginning, keep it simple. Chain together simple punch, kick, knee, and elbow combos.

The following combos are examples you can start with. They are done in shadow boxing practice. This allows you to get the technique down and to learn to follow though. All of these combos can be practices on a heavy bag, suitcase pad, Thai pad, or focus mitts (each combo to their appropriate training item).

Combo 1: jab, cross, front uppercut, rear round kick

Combo 2: high rear kick, high rear kick, low rear kick (special combo)

Combo 3: cross, front uppercut, rear high kick

Jab, Cross, Front Uppercut, Rear Round Kick

Figure 185: Start in stance.

Figure 186: Throw the jab.

Figure 187: Throw the cross.

Figure 188: Throw the uppercut.

Figure 189: Throw the rear round kick.

Figure 190: Follow thorough.

High Rear Kick, High Rear Kick, Low Rear Kick

Figure 191: This combination is designed to teach you to follow through with the round kick.

Figure 192: Throw a high round kick. If you can throw it at head level, then do so. If not, throw it as high as you can safely reach.

Figure 193: Follow through. This image shows me spinning out of the "missed" kick.

Figure 194: I have spun out of the kick and am in a southpaw stance.

Figure 195: I return to my orthodox stance and prepare for the next kick.

Figure 196: I throw the high kick again.

Figure 197: I spin through...

Figure 198: Allowing my body to follow the natural spin path.

Figure 199: I land in the southpaw stance.

Figure 200: I return to my orthodox stance.

Figure 201: I quickly reset and throw the low kick.

Figure 202: I follow through and land in the southpaw stance. This is a great way to learn to follow through. When performed on a heavy bag or suitcase pad it is great for generating speed and leg dexterity.

Cross, Front Uppercut, Rear High Kick

Figure 203: Start from your basic stance.

Figure 204: Throw the cross to the face.

Figure 205: Throw the uppercut to the chin.

Figure 206: Throw the high kick.

Figure 207: Follow through.

Cross, Front Uppercut, Rear Low Kick

Figure 208: Start in your standard stance.

Figure 209: Throw the cross.

Figure 210: Throw the uppercut.

Figure 211:Throw the low kick.

Figure 212: Follow through.

Jab, Cross, Front Elbow, Rear Elbow

Figure 213: Start in stance.

Figure 214: Throw the jab.

Figure 215: Throw the cross.

Figure 216: Throw the front elbow.

Figure 217: Throw the rear elbow. This combo is good if you are closing distance on an opponent.

I have a few final thoughts on shadow boxing. In these images, you will notice that I sometimes look toward my imaginary target and other times I look down. There is a reason for doing both. Whenever you are face to face with someone in a fight, you want to keep your eyes on the target. This allows you to see what they are doing in order to attack and defend properly.

Now, the reason I look down during some of the shadow boxing is to get a feel for the placement. I like to throw the punches and feel where they should be without seeing them. Sometimes I will throw the punch and stop it at the end of the strike. I will the look up to see if it is in proper form. This is kind of a personal form check. Sometimes I even close my eyes and just feel the movement. I have even applied this concept to grappling. I have practiced blind grappling, which is grappling while wearing a blindfold, to test how programmed moves are. This is not for everyone.

Use it if you feel comfortable and only after you have a solid understanding for the moves.

Conclusion: What's Next?

The preceding was a basic introduction to kickboxing, and (by default) boxing. It is meant to give you an idea of proper stance, movement, defense, and striking. It is not meant to teach you how to beat people up or be a bully. It is designed to teach you a form of self-defense and a way to stay fit. It is not meant to give you a cocky feeling so that you can act like a jerk. It is meant to build your confidence.

Moving forward you will need to practice quite a bit to get these techniques down. Once you do, you will have a well-rounded standup striking skill set. Make your training fun. If you do this, you are more likely to stick with it. One thing that can make training fun is to find a training partner who wants to learn with you but does not bring ego to training. Training needs to be cooperative and ego can get in the way of this.

Another way to make training fun is to avoid monotonous training. When I first started, I spent countless hours doing bag work and it was terrible. Did it help me learn? Well yeah, but once my training was mixed up I found it more enjoyable.

Here are some ideas for how to approach training:

- It is not an all effort all the time. Hitting the bag or training pads with 100% power every time will only wear you out and is not the best way to learn technique. Nice and easy is the way to go. The power will come.
- Do no more than one hour of training at a time, especially when training alone. If you have a

159

partner this time can increase because both of you will be doing the work. However, you should still ease into it.

- Organize your workouts in rounds. A stopwatch or timer will work for this purpose. iPods, Android devices, and other portable media devices usually have some sort of timer application. I personal use on from the iTunes store. It cost me a dollar. Set rounds at 3 or 5 minutes with a minute of rest between.

- Start your workouts with a solid warm-up such as vigorous footwork training and shadow boxing, a light run, or a dynamic warm-up. This will heat the muscles up and loosen them in the process. This will accelerate the heart and prep the body for work. Make this the first 2 – 4 rounds of your workout, depending on the round length. Follow the warm-up with some light pad or bag work and then work into heavy work. Use the last few rounds of your workout as a cool down. Do some shadow boxing or some footwork. End the workout with stretching.

That is all. You are ready to get to it. Be respectful of yourself and training partners. This leads to better training relationships and better results. Have fun and always train safe.

About the Expert

Nathan DeMetz is a personal trainer from Indiana. He has long been an avid fitness enthusiast and became a martial arts practitioner in recent years. He has been weight lifting for 12 years and practicing martial arts for three. Nathan is a Certified Personal Trainer (CPT)/Certified Fitness Trainer (CFT) with the International Sports Sciences Association (ISSA). He is a Certified Fitness Kickboxing Instructor through the Kickboxing Fitness Institute.

Nathan is currently pursuing Sport Nutrition Certification through ISSA. Nathan had the opportunity to meet and learn from a USAPL state ranked power lifter, two NPC bodybuilding competitors, and other local, amateur, and competitive athletes. He is the owner/operator of Nathan DeMetz Personal Training and the associated website, nathandemetz.com. Nathan has previously published "How To Jiu Jitsu For Beginners - Your-By-Step Guide To Jiu Jitsu For Beginners".

In 2010, Nathan started his martial arts journey with private boxing lessons from a local instructor before moving on to Muay Thai and jiu-jitsu. He is a white belt in jiu-jitsu and has 3 years of combined kickboxing experience. Nathan always looks to improve his skills through research, one-on-one conversation, and practical application.

Nathan competed in small-scale local competitions though he is not a competitive athlete in general. He simply enjoys the thrill of learning and practicing new forms of martial arts, as well as the rush he gets from weight lifting. Personal bests in weight training include a 500-lb. squat, 345-lb. bench, and a 530-lb. deadlift at a bodyweight between 185 lbs to 213 lbs.

Outside of athletics, Nathan is a family man and everyday guy. He has a 2-year Business degree that he has used in management and now uses as a self-employed contractor. He primarily provides Internet based services to online clients. His list of clients includes Google, Ask.com and eBay. He is married and has been with his wife, Grace, for almost 7 years. Nathan has a daughter from a previous relationship who will be sixteen this year.

Away from work and training, Nathan enjoys spending time with his wife and daughter. He also enjoys fat burgers with French fries and juicy steaks.

HowExpert publishes quick 'how to' guides on all topics from A to Z by everyday experts. Visit HowExpert.com to learn more.

Recommended Resources

- HowExpert.com – Quick 'How To' Guides on All Topics from A to Z by Everyday Experts.
- HowExpert.com/free – Free HowExpert Email Newsletter.
- HowExpert.com/books – HowExpert Books
- HowExpert.com/courses – HowExpert Courses
- HowExpert.com/clothing – HowExpert Clothing
- HowExpert.com/membership – HowExpert Membership Site
- HowExpert.com/affiliates – HowExpert Affiliate Program
- HowExpert.com/writers – Write About Your #1 Passion/Knowledge/Expertise & Become a HowExpert Author.
- HowExpert.com/resources – Additional HowExpert Recommended Resources
- YouTube.com/HowExpert – Subscribe to HowExpert YouTube.
- Instagram.com/HowExpert – Follow HowExpert on Instagram.
- Facebook.com/HowExpert – Follow HowExpert on Facebook.

MENIERE MAN
AND THE ASTRONAUT

THE
SELF-HELP
BOOK FOR
MENIERE'S
DISEASE

PAGE ADDIE PRESS
GREAT BRITAIN
Copyright©2016

Contents

Meniere Man
And The
Astronaut

If you have been diagnosed with Meniere's disease, you're in good company. There have been many famous Meniere sufferers, such as Martin Luther the Augustinian monk, Beethoven the composer, Vincent Van Gogh the artist, Jonathan Swift the author, Peggy Lee the singer, Emily Dickinson the poet, Tim Conley the professional golfer, Dana White the UFC boss, Huey Lewis the singer/songwriter, Kyle Walpole the climber, Alan Shepard the astronaut, and yours truly!

In *The Self-Help Book For Meniere's Disease*, I have written down aspects relevant to people diagnosed with Meniere's. All the books are based on my personal experience of having had Meniere's disease.

When I was diagnosed with Meniere's

disease, I was forty-six. A fit man at the height of my professional career, a partner in a multi-million dollar business, happily married, with a young family of two. I had climbed a long way up the career ladder, thinking the only way was up. Little did I know how hard I would fall. Meniere's caused me to lose my career and material stability.

Not only was it devastating news to be diagnosed, but it was extremely difficult to know what to do or how to cope. I wasn't given any real answers about Meniere's disease. Medical professionals don't agree on the prognosis or outcome of Meniere's. This makes it difficult for sufferers to know the present or plan the future. Meniere's comes as a bewildering shock.

At the time of my diagnosis, there was little information about the disease or how to manage the symptoms. There were a few medical books on the subject which gave me no idea what to expect or how to manage the condition effectively. What I did know was the acute attacks of vertigo were breaking my spirit. As well as trying to cope with vertigo attacks, the loss of life's equilibrium gave me an increasing worry about where Meniere's disease was taking my family and me.

For the first time in my life, I had a constant sense of anxiety and fear. I was at a complete loss. The specialists and doctors couldn't give me definitive answers on how to manage the condition. So how would I cope and get well again? I decided to take responsibility for figuring out how to overcome this condition.

How would I go from Meniere sufferer to Meniere survivor? Life had thrown its curve ball. Meniere's made a massive impact on my life but I did make a full recovery. Working through the condition from illness to wellness has enabled me to help others, and write the Meniere Man series of books.

There is a saying, "It takes one to know one." Unlike a medical text, this book is from the point-of-view of someone who has been there. I know the boundaries of this demanding disease. I understand what you are going through. I have been in the depths of despair. In my mind, I associate Meniere attacks as the most frightening experiences of my life. The out-of-control vertigo creates emotional, mental, social, and physical uncertainty. But despite diagnosis, you will be able, through determination and effort, to regain a sense of power, and equilibrium in your life, when you have hope.

As human beings, we need to have control over our lives, and confidence in where we are going. Not being in control unnerves us. Not being able to find answers exasperates the anxiety we feel. The more anxious we get, the worse we feel. We get lost in the symptoms of Meniere's disease, but having the right information can be a map back to our sense of inherent well-being.

In times of serious illness, we need hope and a belief in a positive outcome. Hope and belief give us the strength to overcome the inertia of disabling effects.

I not only understand the devastating effects of having Meniere's disease, but how Meniere's can have a beneficial impact. Meniere's makes you listen to your body. When you pay attention, you find ways to improve your overall physical and psychological health. You can end up in a better state of health than before you were diagnosed.

By sharing what has worked for me, I hope that you will be able to re-construct your life as quickly as possible. In time, you will be able to do the seemingly impossible. You will be able to fast-track the journey to recovery by understanding Meniere's. Once you know the antagonist, you can mitigate Meniere's symptoms.

When I first had Meniere's, I couldn't look up without going dizzy. I couldn't tie my shoelaces without feeling woozy. I never imagined I would get back to normal, let alone learn to snowboard and windsurf. Yet, it was these balancing activities that helped me regain my equilibrium. The more you do, the better you feel. The more you try, the more you achieve. One step at a time on the road to recovery. Until, it will be you going where you dreamed of going. It will be you —completely well again.

Why Meniere's

The Medical profession has been trying since 1861 to find the cause and cure for Meniere's disease. But Meniere's has proven to be an elusive condition to cure. However, the effect on the person with Meniere's is anything but elusive. Meniere's is a very confrontational and challenging disease.

What didn't elude me was the impact Meniere's was having on my life, but there was more to come. The vertigo attacks became worse by the day. I also suffered severe tinnitus. The sound was inside my head, and I couldn't turn it off. A terrible continually roaring sound, like being trapped inside a 747 airliner, the cabin filled with cicadas combined with the constant roar of jet engines. Meniere's, with its vertigo attacks and associated tinnitus, was tough to cope with.

My days were full of fear. At times, I was

afraid to open my eyes and start another day. A slight movement of my head on the pillow, or turning over in the early hours of the morning, gave me a dizzy, sick feeling. Another day, a repeat of the day before and the weeks before that. The fear factor came in hyper-drive. The fear of spontaneous spinning. Fear of being unable to concentrate. Fear of failing in my business. All this compounding anxiety turned into financial fear. Fear of family disruption. Fear of people thinking less of me.

Communicating with people became an issue. I had constant trouble hearing what people were saying to me. Always yawning and feeling tired. I must have appeared vague, staring blankly, as if disinterested in the conversation. Even my family lost patience. They couldn't understand how I was feeling and just wanted me to be my old self.

Within months, I knew I was failing in my business. The random nature of attacks meant I would suddenly start to spin in a meeting. Late night post-production in small studio spaces with artificial lighting, often caused me to excuse myself and leave a job unfinished. I was running out of excuses.

I knew I couldn't continue in my business with the stress, the overwhelming exhaustion from acute vertigo attacks. I was a key member of the company. I felt embarrassed and threatened by what was happening. Clients' and staff relied on me to make the right decisions. The competitive nature of the business meant that other agencies were always hunting our business.

In that competitive environment, I was aware I was the sick one —the weakest link. My pride would not let me admit to my business partners, and clients, that I had an incurable disease. The symptoms were causing me to fail miserably. Unable to function in my job, I knew I would have to leave the company.

I made a plan to exit with as little disruption to the business as possible. A few months later, this is precisely what I did. I didn't think Meniere's gave me any choice. I was too ill to contemplate anything else. I took a blinkered approach to my future because of how I was feeling. I woke up each morning feeling as hopeless as I did the morning before.

I left the business at the height of my professional career. I existed for a while on monthly checks from an income protection plan. I had paid hundreds of thousands of dollars to protect eighty percent of my income from unexpected illness or accident. Some years later, the insurers suddenly canceled payments two weeks before Christmas. I thought that was unfair. A year later, I litigated against the insurance company for not honoring the income protection policy. The case took nearly five years and eventually I lost all family assets to lawyers. In so many ways, the diagnosis of Meniere's disease changed my life dramatically. It is not just the physical nature of the disease, as it affects the body, but also how it affects people around you —family, friends, and unfortunately for some, fortunes and a secure financial future. The lesson is to surround yourself with empathetic, altruistic, kind, selfless people to help you, and your family.

What Is Meniere's Disease

Meniere's was identified as a condition in 1861 by a French physician by the name of Prosper Meniere. It's a fancy name for a fearful condition. Meniere's is described as 'an incurable disease which has no known cause or origin.' Meniere's is an idiopathic syndrome of endolymphatic hydrops. This is the medical definition: Idiopathic means, unknown cause. Endolymphatic refers to endolymph, a fluid in the inner ear. Hydrops means excessive fluid build-up. When you put it all together - idiopathic endolymphatic hydrops means, the unknown cause of excessive endolymphatic fluid build-up in the inner ear. This build-up of fluid and its consequent flooding effect is what causes the symptoms of vertigo, tinnitus, and progressive deafness.

The condition with all its vertigo, vomiting and spinning, is still not clearly understood by specialists today. The underlying cause of Meniere disease can only be speculative. Meniere's disease is unpredictable, which makes diagnosis and management extremely difficult.

Every person with Meniere's has a different cascade of symptoms. However, although there are primary symptoms, there is an infinite variety of presentations and timing. Some specialists, however, say they can cure or eradicate the symptoms with surgery or invasive procedures. I was not convinced, and in my case, I managed the symptoms by taking a practical, pragmatic and mindful approach.

Diagnosis Of Meniere's Disease

Meniere's can only be identified, with certainty after death by histopathologic study of the temporal bones. Fortunately for patients, it can also be diagnosed while you are alive by identifying spontaneous episodic vertigo attacks, measurable hearing loss, aural fullness, and tinnitus. These are the internationally accepted criteria for a Meniere's disease diagnosis.

For a doctor or specialist to diagnose Meniere's, a patient must have had at least two definite rotational vertigo attacks of twenty minutes or longer. Rotational means spinning horizontally, like swinging a weight around on the end of a rope. The spinning creates a sensation of catastrophic spinning going around and around.

Vertigo

Vertigo, the spinning movement, usually makes you feel nauseous to the point of vomiting or retching. However, you do not and will not lose consciousness. During the attack of vertigo, horizontal rotary nystagmus is always active (the eyes involuntarily flicking from side to side). This type of vertigo is termed episodic vertigo of the Meniere's type.

Hearing Loss

Hearing loss is a major symptom in Meniere's. Typically, the hearing loss is in the lower frequencies. You'll be missing fragments of conversation if there is background sound like kitchen clatter, music, or television. You'll have difficulty understanding what people are saying. You will first notice your hearing has dropped in these everyday situations. This may only be an impression, as tinnitus or aural fullness can make it feel like your hearing is down. How much you think you have lost will be subjective.

An comprehensive examination in an audio clinic determines hearing loss. Your hearing may or may not fluctuate in the early stages of Meniere's disease. That's why your hearing loss must be documented by an audio-metric test to satisfy the criteria set by your ENT (ear, nose, and throat) specialist. The specific loss has to be identified in the affected ear, at least on one occasion, by an audiometric test. Your specialist will make a diagnosis of Meniere's disease based on specific technical recordings.

Aural Fullness

You will experience aural fullness. This feels like having a soft wad of damp cotton wool inside your ear, blocking sound out. The sensation of fullness is the fluid pressure building up in the inner ear. The symptom of aural fullness can be a useful marker for you. It can signal that a vertigo attack is imminent.

When your hearing is down, you are likely to be in the zone (vulnerable to having an acute Meniere's episode). Cut back immediately on all activities and take a physical rest as a preventative measure. Once you are aware of this symptom, you can counter the possibility of having an attack by immediately reducing stress physically, mentally, or emotionally.

Tinnitus

Tinnitus is usually described as a roaring sound. Tinnitus for Meniere's sufferers is created by damage to the cilia, the fine hairs in your inner ear that help transmit sound to the brain. When you have an vertigo attack, the endolymph chamber is flooded with endolymph fluid, which damages cilia hairs in the cochlea. These little hairs send electrical impulses to the brain, and once they are damaged, they don't regenerate. So unfortunately, the brain fills the void with a constant roaring sound called tinnitus.

I relate tinnitus to being in the void of some industrial underworld wasteland, where the sound of roaring central air conditioning is on twenty-four hours, seven days a week. I recall one particular day in the Rocky Mountains, a bright, crisp blue sky above pristine natural wilderness. Dark green fir tree branches covered with a light dusting of snow. I was standing alone in deep powder snow, not a living soul around. My eyes could see the still quietness, but the noise from my tinnitus was deafening!

The Benefits Of Tinnitus

The good news is, through sleep and deep relaxation, you can achieve a respite from the constant noise. I now don't feel worried about the tinnitus. Tinnitus can be used as a very sensitive warning signal. An increase in tinnitus volume means your body is under stress. When tinnitus increases in volume, think back to what you have just eaten. Did you consume hidden salt, chili, sugar, caffeine, or alcohol? What stress have you been under lately? Take a closer look at the demands, pressures, stresses of your daily life.

You need to be a detective, then put whatever you decide was a possible cause on your list of things to avoid. Take serious note, alter activities, and take time to become aware and take action. When tinnitus rings in your head, you are overdoing things. You should stop and rest. The more positive your focus, the less of a problem tinnitus is. Listening to your body works twofold. You help reduce the tinnitus as well as the possibility of a vertigo attack.

The attitude of using positive recruitment for all Meniere symptoms is one of the most constructive pro-active things you can do towards better health. Most people don't have the benefit of tinnitus and consequently push their bodies over the limit. Only then finding they've become chronically ill with a disease, like arterial sclerosis or heart disease. Instead of getting depressed or down on the condition, use it as a learning tool for getting better and having an overall healthier life.

Time And Money Matters

People diagnosed with an incurable illness react in different ways. Depending on their personalities, some pretend it isn't happening, refusing to accept that they are ill. In contrast, others share the bad news and find comfort with family and friends. As an active, physical man, I found the diagnosis almost impossible to accept.

I saw it as a life failure. I was embarrassed to admit that I had a weakness. I wanted to hide the condition. When it came down to my work-life, I didn't reveal my health situation, mainly because I was confused about the full effects of Meniere's. My decision however was a game-changer and is a marked regret in my life.

My suggestion is to do the opposite. Come out into the open and have some trust that there are enough good people around to support you.

Being able to work with symptoms of Meniere's and still perform at the same level can be a challenge. If you can't take a break from your job, then at the very least, cut back on the amount of work you are doing. Have other people step in and take over. This is the time to delegate tasks and share the load to free you up. I know it is the last thing you want to do, but symptoms will only escalate to the negative if you don't. Cutting down hours means less in your pay packet. A little less money and more time will give you a chance to survive financially and more time to work on your health. Always let people know if you're not feeling up to the task at hand.

The fact is, there needs to be changes. You may have to negotiate your way into a position with fewer demands. You will have to let your employers know how this condition is affecting you. If you are self-employed, take less money and hire someone to help you. You will need to cut back on work. You become less reliable in the workplace when you can't predict how you will feel physically. You may not be able to show up every day for work. You may have to call in sick or leave work early. Don't hide the fact that you are having trouble with this condition. Support and understanding are precisely what you need.

From experience, this is the time to make significant decisions. Accept, for a while, you won't be able to function as you did before

Meniere's. If necessary, seek advice from a variety of professional sources, arbitrators, counselors, lawyers, and medical specialists. Use more than one source to put your puzzle together. Then go and talk with your employer or partners. Face working with Meniere's head on, and chin up.

Meniere's causes a definite change in financial circumstances. If my experience helps just one of you to keep what you've worked for, this book will have been well worth the effort. If I had accepted the financial affects of Meniere's, I would have restructured things so I could allow myself the time off work without impacting and draining personal resources. I would not have left my position in the company and given up my career. I left my job because I did not understand that I could recover from an incurable disease. I thought I would never get better.

Personal circumstances are different, but there are a few basic things you can do here. My advice is to immediately look at household budgets and mortgages, then restructure, cut back, or downsize. Meniere's will bring unexpected changes in your financial status, especially if you are the primary earner. You may have to change jobs or quit, rely on your partner's income, borrow money, downsize the house, cut back on expenses, give up luxuries, sell the second car. This is a reality. You will have medical expenses, like doctors, specialists, and pharmacy costs. Take into account accruing medical bills.

Plan to restructure your present life. The change Meniere brings to a household, and the time needed to recover, means you must make definite decisions early in your recovery plan. Use your intuition coupled with information to determine your future.

How can you manage to spend time doing this and still look after financial obligations? You will need time to recover from Meniere's. Time is money. So you have to figure out how to 'buy' enough time to allow you to have a break from work. You will need at least three years working on your health, to get better. It may not be as you dreamed; it may be better. Take your time. Face the situation and act.

My advice is to make significant changes for the long-haul. You need to put measures in place to protect your assets because this is not like having flu for a few weeks. It is not like a heart bypass, where you need a few months. Don't be tempted to rely on others, like income protection insurers. At the end of the day, they may not be as supportive as you would expect, and if you rely on them, and they let you down, the effect can be financially disastrous.

Meniere's At Home

Having more time for yourself is key to recovery. At home, do more for yourself and less for others in the early days. This is one time you need to think about your needs. Put 'you' first, whenever you can. If it's your pattern to do everything to support everyone else, you won't be able to continue doing that. If shouldering the world is your habit, you need to learn to ask for help and sit back a bit.

You will need time out to do activities just for yourself. A walk. A long soak in a warm tub. Try to move away from stress as much as you can. To do this, you need to let people around you know how you are feeling. Then they can make adjustments to help you.

Doing more for yourself is not a selfish act. When you have Meniere's, it comes down to self-preservation and finding a balance. Imagine everything in your life is compartmentalized, in equal measure —family, work, rest, time-out, chores, holidays. Now, imagine giving a few of the things you usually do (and the stress that goes with then) over to someone else at this juncture in your life. You simply cannot be a doer of all things. Just thinking about this is a start.

Once you reduce your obligations to others, you can do something for yourself. Even if you do just one thing for yourself a day. Every positive thing you do will count towards recovery. The more you can do for yourself in the early stages of Meniere's, the better the prognosis. If you are waiting to feel better to start, my advice is don't wait. Start now, and be on your way to recovery!

The Pharmacy

The drugs prescribed for Meniere's sufferers differ from specialist to specialist and country to country. Read up and discuss your drug options with your doctor or specialist.

You will need to discuss which drugs will be best for you. Understand how specific drugs work and how they affect your body long term. It is essential to find out as much as you can. Everybody is different, but here's a list of the prescribed drugs I took. On diagnosis of Meniere's, my specialist prescribed Serc, (Betahistine) a blood stimulator, Kaluril (Amiloride), a diuretic, Stemetil, an anti- nausea drug to help relieve the symptoms of an acute attack. He also prescribed Urea to stop the attacks as soon as they started.

Serc is the brand name for the chemical Betahistine. This drug is known to improve blood flow to the labyrinth (the bone capsule, which protects and surrounds the inner ear). It is believed there may be a micro-circulatory dysfunction in the inner ear due to damage done by Meniere's attacks. This means the normally independent circulatory system of the inner ear is not functioning effectively, and blood flow is not efficient in the inner ear.

At the time, Betahistine was one of those controversial drugs, discussed at length as to its effectiveness in treating Meniere's symptoms. In some trials, the results indicated that not taking Betahistine was just as effective. If I forgot to take a dose, I'd experience an increase in tinnitus and a woozy unstable feeling. Initially, these symptoms were enough for me to continue with Betahistine. Eventually, I reduced the dosage until I no longer took any. I did this despite my doctor saying I would need to take it daily for the rest of my life. After I reduced the dosage down and came off the medication, no symptoms returned. Check with your own doctor first.

Again, my advice is based on my personal experience. In the realm of what drugs to take, or not, it is a personal decision. Talk with your doctor and monitor the effectiveness of drugs and be aware of possible side-effects.

Kaluri is the brand name for the chemical Amiloride. Its primary objective is to increase urinary water loss, which flushes out sodium (salt). Diuretics are documented to cause the loss of potassium in the process of flushing out the fluids. Potassium is essential for the proper functioning of the kidneys, heart, nerves, and digestive system. Amiloride is often prescribed as a diuretic for long term use, as it retains potassium in the body. It's called a potassium-sparing drug. Also, if you take diuretics regularly, you need to either take a potassium-sparing drug or include potassium supplements in your diet. In addition, eat a potassium-rich diet with foods such as garlic, onions, and prunes. You can make potassium- rich broth, from vegetables like onions, garlic, carrots, and potatoes.

Diuretics, if taken for longer than six months, can dramatically drop your levels of folic acid. Lack of folic acid creates a toxic amino acid associated with the hardening of the arteries. So, if you suffer from high cholesterol as well, consider taking folic acid as a supplement. You can eat foods rich in folic acid. Many kinds of breakfast cereal have folic acid added.

Taking the drug Urea can be useful for stopping attacks. Urea is a dehydrating drug. So when taken, it dramatically sucks any fluid out of the inner ear. Urea needs to be taken five minutes or so before an attack happens, for it to be effective. If you are attuned to your attacks and get warning signals, like increased tinnitus, aural fullness, or a noticeable decrease in hearing, Urea may stop the impending attack. When taken before important meetings or events, Urea might enable you to participate with confidence. Urea could prevent an attack for approximately three hours. Then when the three hours are up, one is vulnerable to an attack.

How long one would use Urea for, is debatable. You have to consider the long term effects on the kidneys. When considering this option, talk to your doctor.

Stemetil is an anti-nausea drug used in the treatment of Meniere's vertigo symptoms. This drug can minimize the impact of spinning and nausea. Stemetil can be administered by injection.

Surgical Options

When it comes to surgical options, there is no such thing as tried and true. New procedures are not necessarily breakthrough procedures. Elective surgery is a very personal decision. I didn't opt for surgery to relieve symptoms, but I know many sufferers do. The more I looked into surgery as an option, the more I realized that surgeons were continually changing their views on the effectiveness of procedures. This was backed up by my specialist. I asked him about his views on the efficacy of surgery; he said that treatments vary depending on the surgeon because so much is unknown about the condition. This made me stop and think very carefully about surgical options.

The lymphatic sac shunt was the first operation to be offered to me. Explained as an out-patient procedure to preserve hearing and relieve vertigo. The probability of having the surgery again a year later is highly likely, as the shunt has a tendency to become blocked and needs replacing. As I understand, the shunt is now seen as a procedure rated by some, as having no more benefit than doing nothing at all.

Another option is Vestibular Neurectomy. I talked with a friend who had this operation hoping for quick relief from Meniere's symptoms. He said the surgery includes cutting the vestibular nerve. The vestibular nerve is the nerve of balance. By cutting this nerve, vertigo sensations are not transmitted to the brain's balancing receptors. However, this is really radical surgery.

After this surgery, my friend was left permanently deaf in one ear and had to learn to walk again. He told me it was a shattering experience. He wasn't expecting to lose his hearing. He also wasn't prepared for the debilitating effect of having his nerve of balance cut. Having his nerve of balance cut meant he had to undergo extensive long term rehabilitation to learn how to walk again.

He tells me he no longer has dizzy attacks but feels woozy and stumbles from time to time. He said, having no dizzy attacks is fine but used the old cliché, what I gained on the swings I lost on the roundabouts. For him, it was not a win-win situation. The surgical option of Vestibular Neurectomy is supposed to preserve your hearing while stopping vertigo.

Did something go wrong with my friend Rob's operation? There was no turning the clock back. Imagine the shock of having to learn to walk again. He was also supposed to retain the hearing in his ear, which he didn't. Talking to him, he gave me the impression that he was unaware of any possible risks or consequences of surgery. That is why all questions need to be asked before the operation. When you are prepared, you know what to expect.

I decided to stay in control and self manage. This proved to be the correct decision for me. It's a personal choice. Despite acute symptoms, don't be rushed into what may appear to be a solution at the time. If any surgery is being offered to you right now, ask as many questions as you can. Look up the procedures and associated risks. Ask for a second or third opinion. There could be many successful other options to relieve Meniere's suffering. It will be interesting to see if one successful surgical procedure is universally agreed upon in the future. One that guarantees results with no downsides.

There are theories about the inner-ear's immune system being partly involved in Meniere's disease. The endolymphatic sac is the immune organ of the ear. This theory of immune system involvement in Meniere's has created a trend towards surgical procedures aimed at damaging the endolymphatic sac.

The theory is, if the lymphatic sac is damaged, the immune function of the ear will be suppressed; inhibiting the immune function and, consequently, Meniere's attacks. On the surface, this seems logical. The procedure is to damage the sac using a series of Gentamicin injections. Injections of Gentamicin are given through the eardrum. Four injections are administered in a month, effectively stopping dizziness for approximately a year. This procedure effectively deadens the ear but it also leaves the sufferer with profound hearing loss. If dizziness returns, the procedure is to have another series of injections.

What Causes Meniere's Disease

There are many anecdotal reasons for the cause of Meniere's, especially from sufferers. Having an answer to 'why me?' is a fundamental psychological building block towards a full recovery. In my case, this was definitely true. I looked at my life and put a raft of experiences together. From a car accident to a sports injury, the body retains a body-memory of every accident or illness. Investigate your history as a therapeutic exercise to find possible causes.

As for the cause of Meniere's, the medical professionals state that Meniere's disease has no known cause and no known origin. They are researching and investigating the possibility of causes arising from physical trauma as in head injuries, viral infections of the inner ear, hereditary predisposition, and allergies.

Recently, researchers have been looking at the immunologic function of the endolymphatic sac; they think immune system diseases may also be a factor. However, the underlying cause of Meniere's disease is still unknown. The research is ongoing.

Despite this I always felt a need to have a sense of knowing. Understanding gives us personal power. Accepting your hypothesis on why you have Meniere's, means you can move forward to recovery.

Doing
Life With
Meniere's
Disease

Unfortunately, Meniere's will be associated with some of the most frightening experiences of your life. The out of control nature creates social, psychological, and physical uncertainty. There is a lot of anxiety and fear associated with Meniere's. Any hint of a vertigo attack gave me a cold sweat and a racing heart! I have been there, and it's terrifying. Bravery is needed daily.

How can 'normal' people, your doctor, your partner, your boss or friends, your insurer, understand the whirling dervish, the tumbling into hyperspace, and the continual roar of jet engines in your head, along with vomiting, and deafness? As my doctor said, Meniere's is aggressive and confrontational. That's because it arrives without warning, and it's right there inside your head.

I remember learning to sail a yacht once, and the tutor told me she never had anyone seasick on her boat. Why? Because I tell people exactly where they are going, the route they are taking, and estimated time of arrival, she explained. I make a simple analogy here. We need to know where we're going, or we tend to get anxious, frightened, or panic. We need to have a sense of direction and knowledge of outcomes for our well-being and health.

Meniere casts you adrift, with no charts. We move rudderless into deep uncharted waters. Our personal compass no longer registers magnetic north. During an acute attack, our compass of certainty spins out of control. That's the reality of Meniere's disease.

To counter this effect, we must get back a sense of control. And we can, by being aware of ourselves in relation to symptoms. From this, you can make plans with Meniere's. Nothing changed in my condition until the moment I changed my thinking about Meniere's disease. Until the day, I decided to stand up to it and not let the disease rule my life. I began to fight back, using my will-power, hope, faith, and trust.

I call it getting and maintaining the right attitude. First, I was determined not to end up shuffling around in slippers. I made a pact with myself that my life was not going to be relegated to a tracksuit. You must make an agreement —to not give in, give up, or surrender to the condition. Don't let Meniere's consume your life.

So start by taking notes. Get a notebook and keep a journal. This is what I did. To gain a sense of control, I started writing everything down. I began to self-monitor and figure out what was causing the attacks. While making my journal notes, I figured out ways to manage everything from triggers to coping methods and further, how to move forward and regain a full life, without surgical intervention.

Change your mind-set. Think of yourself as an adventurer in unknown territory. You don't and won't give up on getting better. Determination is key. Do not limit yourself to feeling bad about the situation. Make a positive move towards improving aspects of your current life. Making a move in the right direction mentally and physically makes all the difference to the outcome.

I believe I managed to counterbalance and minimize the long term effects of vestibular deterioration through physical exercise, diet, vitamins, alternative therapies, and a positive attitude. Keep hold of hope. Creating and maintaining a personal regime is crucial. It puts you back in control. By doing so, you are making a definite decision not to stay as you are.

By sheer creative momentum, you are

creating a counterweight to balance Meniere's, and by doing so, you will move forward. This is my philosophy, and it works.

Create your health regime and guarantee yourself a positive outcome. There is a lot you can do to balance your life and improve your way of life. Some call it mind over matter. Rather than accepting your situation, take specific actions to improve your health. A will to get better is necessary. Rather than accepting your situation, take specific measures to improve your health.

My philosophy on health is this: To effect permanent change, you have to look holistically at all aspects of your life. This is essential.

The secret to recovery is this, 'You can't wait until you feel better to start.' You must move in the direction of health through exercise, diet and attitude. Don't wait until you 'feel like' doing things. You have to tell your body to get going. At this point, something tangible starts to happen to turn things around. You stop your body from accepting the condition as a permanent state of being. You tell your body not to stagnate, you will be healthy again. You need to adopt the attitude —you can and will get better. Take control of your health and be consistent.

Feeling down and negative suppresses the natural ability of the body to heal itself. Don't be phased by days that are symptom heavy. These days will become a thing of the past. Soon, you will notice attacks are less frequent, the intensity is less, and gaps between attacks are greater. The fewer attacks you have, the more normal you feel, the more hopeful you become. The idea is to instigate positive change on a cellular level. Your body will take note of the changes and start to respond with positive health.

I am not trying to educate medical people in the actual physiology of Meniere's disease. My Ear Nose and Throat specialist told me, "The cause of Meniere's is unknown and the treatments manifold, therefore straight medicine alone does not hold all the answers if indeed it holds any at all. Alternative ways of helping a long-standing, ongoing, variable condition can be helpful."

No matter how hard and difficult things are for you right now, it won't be like this forever. By making pro-active changes you will improve your health. Then Meniere's disease will not rule every moment of your life, as it may do now.

Triggers For Meniere Attacks

Here's a hot question amongst Meniere's sufferers. What does trigger attacks? Are attacks indeed triggered?

People with Meniere's are sure attacks are triggered (caused by something specific). Still, there is no scientific proof to back up this hypothesis. That, of course, doesn't mean there aren't triggers. In fact, I think there are.

When you have attacks, you want to know why they occurred, so you can stop the same thing happening again. Keep a journal to figure things out. The triggers for attacks are personal interpretations of situations and events that repeat themselves over a long time. You can work out your triggers by observing what you were doing before an attack. Then see if this is a repeated pattern. Once you discern triggers for your attacks, avoid the situations, or adapt the criteria to minimize their effects. It's that basic. As human beings we find it very hard to accept random events like spontaneous vertigo because they are so disruptive. We want to understand why things happen. Rhyme and reason, we need to have it.

Anything that increases your body's blood fluid volume can cause an attack. You should therefore restrict anything that raises your blood pressure or changes the content of the body's fluid. Foods and spices that can increase your blood fluid volume are chilies, curry, spices, green tea, nitrates in sausages, salami, food coloring, food additives such as monosodium glutamate, excessive sugar, and salt, salted meats, and fish such as kippers, preservatives, blue vein cheeses, processed cheese, Camembert and Brie, strong vintage cheddar, processed foods, wine, caffeine, and spicy foods. Even emotional stress affect body fluid levels.

Noise Stress

Did you know the human body never adapts to loud sudden noises or vertigo? The body will adapt to most other sensory changes but never to those two. That is why sound is so stressful and listed as a psychological stressor by psychologists. Loud constant sounds in certain cafes or restaurants, dog barking, babies crying, electrical tools, and fireworks can stress you out.

As you progress through Meniere's and experience more hearing loss, you will find certain environmental sounds become extremely loud. No one else hears it like this, so you have to tell your partner or friends when it's too loud for you. Shift to a quieter corner or change venues because your hearing will not adjust to loud noise.

Physiological Stress

Physical stress on the body can cause problems. Name your stress: dehydration, allergies to dust, pollen, mold, fungus, excessive heat and cold, an approaching thunderstorm with changes in the barometric pressure —all or any may trigger a vertigo attack.

Some physical triggers are invisible to the naked eye. Others are caused by the choices you make, like staying up late, smoking and drinking, spending hours with technology, doing excessive physical exercise or any prolonged activity. When you have Meniere's, you need to be aware that time-frames can be triggers. Get to know your limits. Practice limiting time down to twenty minute intervals. Then take a short break. Don't be tempted to keep going. You want to avoid 'wearing yourself out,' or 'running yourself ragged' as the saying goes. Instead, you are aiming for some self-preservation.

Time-frames apply to any activity, inside or outside the house, from weeding the garden to watching the computer screen. Be aware of the point where you start to feel fatigued. Stop what you are doing and take a break. Then increase this slowly, by small increments, to one hour. Put a clock on what you do. For every hour of constant activity, take a fifteen-minute break. If you keep going and ignore this fact, you will enter into a zone that makes you vulnerable to attacks.

As your health improves, you won't need to monitor the time spent so rigidly. But you will always need to listen to your body.

Eye Stress

Eye stress can be a trigger for attacks. Eye muscles are connected to the vestibular system. So when your vestibular system is damaged, any excessive eye movement affects balance. Even looking up suddenly can make everything spin. Try to look up slowly and control any sudden head movements.

When going to the movies, check your tickets. Make sure you sit in the middle of the back rows. When you can see the edges of the cinema screen you're visually anchored, and not lost in a dark space.

Walking down supermarket aisles is a potential problem. Have you noticed how images flickering on the edge of your vision makes you dizzy? Flickering lights are a problem in stores, shopping malls, public foyers, galleries, airports, and supermarkets. Florescent lighting, flashing, pulsing lights, neon signs, and street lights, create visual disturbance.

You need to come up with creative solutions for light triggers. You can find ways to help cut down light intensity and disturbance created by light variants. You can wear sunglasses. Ask someone else to do the shopping. Replace flickering light tubes. Create ambient lighting using natural light and halogen bulbs on dimmers in your home.

Reduce the amount of time spent scrolling on computer screens. I couldn't work at the computer for more than ten minutes. For me, the computer was a major trigger. If I pushed it, I'd be sure to have a Meniere's attack. I thought sunglasses could be the answer, but sitting in front of a computer with sunglasses on felt weird. So I bought a screen filter to block light intensity. A screen filter helped considerably. In the early days of Meniere's I carefully monitored my time and increased sessions by small increments. Eventually, I was able to spend hours at the computer. To avoid what could arguably be your worst electronic trigger, take regular breaks when working at the computer and pay attention to how tired you feel.

Emotional Stress

Stress just doesn't exist in one form. You can have emotional, and mental stress: arguments, anxiety, worry, shouldering the blame, not letting go of issues, temper flare-ups, guilt, putting pressure on yourself to achieve, all and any self-defeating attitudes. Symptoms of stress can range from tiredness to exhaustion, irritability, loss of concentration, anxiety, and sweaty palms. Don't put up with stress, do something about it. Listen to your body and recognize signs of anxiety. Don't ignore how you are feeling.

Look very carefully at how you are reacting emotionally. Are you emotionally overly excited or frightened? Is your mind racing out of control? Look at everything in your life and see what is causing your stress. Remember, emotional stress is created by the way you think, feel, and react, so by its nature, it is well within your control.

Overload

I have talked to others in the early stages of their condition, and the common attitude to changing the pattern in their life is this: "I can't change anything, people rely on me. I would lose work and get behind. Then I would never get on top of it. There is no one else who can do it for me." This is the same reasoning I gave to a psychologist after she suggested I cut back on my workload, which I didn't initially do.

Meniere's forces you to change. Loading up one stress on top of another is a sure way of aggravating Meniere's. So it's better to take control and cut back on your workload. When you're physically tired, do not stack up a list of tasks to achieve. You must reduce the 'to do' list. Take time out.

If you want to reduce the number of Meniere's attacks you are experiencing, don't overdo one thing to the point of being exhausted. You may have a habit of being a workaholic prior to Meniere's, but you won't get away with it now. Pace yourself where you can. This is so important. Listen to your body. Be ready to back off when your body is telling you it's tired. Never work or play to the point of fatigue, or you can almost guarantee Meniere's will return with a vengeance.

Don't do more than one demanding activity a day. That doesn't mean you can't do other things on the same day but make them undemanding. Try not to spend more time than you need on any one activity.

Do tasks in small time frames. For example, try to limit intense conversations or meetings to approximately fifteen to thirty minutes, then move on to the next activity. Take breaks when working on extended projects that take over an hour, go for a short walk around the house or place of business.

If you want to do something about stress, I found the following book extremely helpful. My survival bible, *Full Catastrophe Living* by Jon Kabat-Zinn, has been my mainstay during troubled times in my life. I read it cover to cover and over and over. You can use the same proven meditation techniques at home that he uses in his stress clinics.

In stressful moments, try and detach yourself from your mind, even for a minute, as though you are watching a stranger. Monitor that person (yourself) objectively. Then consider what you are doing; take decisive, positive action to minimize the stress.

Change your overall attitude and look at all the overload in your life, and find a way of effectively managing it.

Seek help from a professional or read books on coping with overload. Meniere's is a great life teacher. Be aware, if you don't control yourself and monitor your stress, workload, and overload levels, Meniere's will take control. Meniere's is a hard taskmaster.

Mechanics Of
An Attack

You know what it's like to have severe vertigo attacks. What you may not know, is what is happening inside your inner ear. The main areas involved in an attack are the endolymph and perilymph compartments and the Reissner membrane. Each compartment is filled with fluid, which contains potassium and sodium. These two areas are separated by a membrane called the Reissner membrane. What happens during an attack is this: the fluid volume in the endolymph cavity (potassium-rich) expands and encroaches into and reduces the volume of the perilymph cavity (potassium-poor). This expansion stretches the separating membrane (Reissner membrane) until it ruptures. Then the fluids of the endolymph and perilymph are mixed. This mixture now floods the vestibular nerve (balance nerve) in the inner ear, which paralyzes it. This paralysis means the brain's signals from the paralyzed nerve in one ear are stopped or very weak. Meanwhile, the unaffected healthy ear is sending out strong, uninterrupted signals. So, what you have is a strong set of signals and a weak set of signals being transmitted to the brain simultaneously. This is registered in the brain as an acute vestibular imbalance. The brain then sends out signals to your body, which results in acute spinning, nausea, heart rate increase, sweating, and often diarrhea. This is the Meniere's attack as you know it.

During the attacks, you would've noticed your eyes flicking back and forth. This action is called nystagmus, an involuntary eye movement, which causes the spinning sensation. The nystagmus is made up of two movements, a rapid movement, and a slow movement. The rapid movement is normally to the unaffected ear and a slow movement to your affected ear.

As the eye muscles are connected directly to the vestibular nerve, this imbalance of nerve signal pulsing directly affects eye movements. A weak pulse on one side results in a slow movement in that direction. A strong pulse from the other ear means a strong movement towards that side. As the eyes start to flick back and forth, you experience the sensation of an uncontrollable spin. These eye movements are incredibly rapid. Nystagmus lasts until the affected vestibular nerve is no longer paralyzed and pulses to the brain, and eyes are restored. It won't and can't last forever, though, at the time, the ongoing sensation feels like it. But the spinning eventually gets to where the eyes are not flicking quite so badly. Ultimately you can focus on a small point on the wall.

The settling down of the eye spinning correlates to the mending of the Reissner membrane and the recovery of the nerve of balance. The attack stops when the membrane is repaired, and the normal balance of potassium and sodium are returned, and the vestibular nerve is no longer bathed in the mixed fluids.

Speedy recovery of the Reissner membrane is obviously an essential part of the process, so anything you can do on a general health level will ensure a speedy recovery. The whole connection between having fewer attacks, less severe symptoms, may be dependent on your overall approach to health. From rest to vitamins and diet, to exercise.

How To Cope During Vertigo

Since that first attack and the many that were to follow, I can now suggest techniques for coping during an attack. The key to coping with attacks and reducing the effect of an acute attack is to find practical ways to stop the panic and the cycle of fear. You do this by minimizing anxiety through mind control.

The mind plays a vital role in the actual attacks of Meniere's. You can minimize anxiety by being positive about the outcome of every attack. Especially throughout the attack. No matter how bad you are feeling. No matter how devastating the vertigo is. Know that the attack will pass. Tell yourself that you will be OK again. If you let the cycle of fear, anxiety, and worry take you away, the Meniere's attack becomes worse.

During an attack, I realized that if I allowed

my mind to focus on how terrifying the ordeal was, the spinning intensified. When I controlled my mind in the attacks and didn't let it get involved in the cycle of fear, the spinning didn't seem as intensive. Detaching the mind from the experience, allows the experience to be what it is —an acute event of limited and ending duration.

Control fear and anxiety, and attacks will appear to be of shorter duration and less intensive. Over time and after experiencing attacks, you learn to accept the fear of the possibility of an attack. You will feel more in control. There will be lesser sense of chaos and more a feeling of coping. When an attack happens, you use breathing techniques and mind control to carry you through. You use positive thinking to tell yourself this will pass. That you are working on your health. Attacks will be less intensive, and the duration shorter. Ultimately you'll have fewer attacks, and eventually none at all.

Why Meniere Affects Hearing

Meniere's is an aggressive condition and is relentless in its destruction of your ear. So how is the hearing mechanism damaged? What happens in the ear to make it lose hearing?

Meniere hearing loss is a sensorineural nerve deafness. During an attack, the cochlear hair cells of the inner ear are bathed in sodium and potassium chemicals due to the sudden rupturing of the Reissner membrane. This rupture occurs every time you have an attack.

Unfortunately, each time you have an attack, there is permanent damage done to the hair cells responsible for transmitting sounds to the brain. These tiny hair cells typically transmit sound via the hearing nerve to the hearing center located within the brain. The resulting damage to the cochlea hair cells means the brain receives incomplete sound messages, and one of the results is tinnitus.

With each attack, more of the delicate hair cells are progressively damaged, their ability to transmit sound is reduced, and your hearing deteriorates. The longer you have Meniere's, the more hearing you lose. The intensity and range of hearing deterioration caused by Meniere's disease are different for everyone. Nobody will experience precisely the same rate or level of deterioration.

After a Meniere's attack, your hearing should return to normal levels. As the disease progresses, your hearing will stop returning to normal levels after an attack. The hearing in the affected ear will become permanently reduced.

Fluctuating Hearing

In the early stages of Meniere's, you will notice how your hearing fluctuates. Up one moment, down the next. This is often accompanied by a sense of fullness in your ear, which doctors call aural fullness. This feels rather like having cotton wool packed deep inside your ear. Sound becomes muffled. Just before an attack, your hearing level will drop, and aural fullness will increase noticeably.

Before being diagnosed with Meniere's

disease, I was talking on the phone to a client. He started giving me details of products. I needed to take notes, but when I swapped the phone to my other ear, I could hardly hear him. I said, "Look, I've got a bad line, I can't hear you very well." I hung up and rang back on another line. When he answered, I still couldn't hear what he was saying. It was only when I swapped the phone over to the other ear, that I could listen to him. What I thought was a faulty line, was a fault in my inner ear. The phone incident was the first time I noticed a real problem with my hearing. This incident prompted me to make an appointment with an ENT specialist and the subsequent diagnosis of Meniere's disease.

While living with Meniere's, I learned to notice any sudden change in hearing and used it as a warning sign. I figured out that if my hearing levels dropped, I was in the zone of a Meniere's attack. So hearing levels became an internal body code I could 'read' as warning signals. I would act immediately, stop what I was doing, and walk away. I would then go and eat or do meditation. Just relax. It can take an hour or two and sometimes 3-4 days for the aural fullness to subside.

When the feeling of fullness went, I would feel 'safe' from an imminent attack. Then I would get back to normal activities. Body signals became part of my management plan to decrease the number of attacks. If you ignore these signals you'll risk more Meniere's symptoms. If you work with symptoms, and understand them as signals, then you can help yourself recover.

As Meniere's progresses, the affected ear loses its dynamic range of hearing. Dynamic range is the ear's ability to cope with quick shifts in sound levels, making normal sounds seem louder than they are. This is called Hyperacusis, a hypersensitivity to normal sounds.

Another reason why normal sounds may be louder is the recruitment factor associated with hearing loss. This is an abnormal perception of loudness. Have you noticed the recruitment factor in a café? You are quietly sipping a decaffeinated latte. The waiter drops a handful of stainless spoons onto the tile floor. You get a super-shock! You are experiencing the recruitment factor.

Cafes are full of spoons and china cups, so try to take a table in a quiet area, well away from extractor fans, kitchen doors, and service areas. You can use protective hearing devices such as custom-made sound diffusers or disposable foam earplugs. These are available from audiologists, hearing centers and drugstores.

Emotional Effect Of Hearing Loss

People with hearing issues, struggle to communicate in social situations. We often miss subtle inflections and guess words, or get the wrong meaning completely. Sometimes, misinterpretation can get you into some funny conversations. At other times, it can be frustrating and detrimental to the business at hand.

Hearing deficit is seen socially as a disability and weakness. And some people refuse to understand. It is also associated with old age and decline of physical powers and abilities. When I was in my forties, I had a hard time coming to terms with permanent loss of hearing and the social impact of being partially deaf.

Deafness in the affected ear is unfortunately unavoidable, as it is the eventual outcome of

Meniere's disease. Given the struggle that comes with hearing impairments, it's not surprising that people with hearing disabilities often become withdrawn and even aggressive.

Looking closely at emotional problems associated with hearing difficulties, you may recognize some of these psychological and physiological effects in your life: fatigue, irritability, embarrassment, tension, stress, anxiety, depression, negativism, avoidance of social activities, withdrawal from personal relationships, rejection, danger to personal safety, general health, loneliness, dissatisfaction with life and unhappiness at work —quite a long list.

Over the years, I have experienced every one of these issues. There is a huge learning curve for everyone involved. Meniere's disease hearing loss can be very antisocial. At one stage, I became isolated within my family. Even with our tightly meshed love connection, my wife and two children often appeared oblivious to communication struggles. Sometimes they did not include me fully in conversations or discussions. I felt sidelined when I misheard them. This made me withdrawn and, for the first time in my life, self-conscious within the family. Often they didn't bother repeating themselves, even when I asked again. Sometimes they chose not to speak loudly enough. My wife said her vocal cords felt strained from raising her voice during conversations. She did have a habit of talking from inside cupboards, or the refrigerator, or from another room. I'm sure my lovely family didn't do this intentionally or with malice! They simply didn't understand the impact it was having on me because I did not actually tell them.

Isolation within the family increased daily. I had to talk to them to help them understand how deafness affected my world. When they finally understood the reality of my disability and the loneliness I felt, things changed. The family gradually became more empathetic, tolerant, patient, and helpful.

Regardless of the condition you have, it's all about support and attitude. Tell people to speak up, or please repeat. Keep the humor going, and have a laugh about the odd words or sentences that sound hilarious. Keep your family and friends involved with the Meniere situation. Don't push them away and don't give up on the social contact. Find a way around any limitations Meniere's creates, until you recover. People will be there for you, but it's up to you to be receptive.

Meniere's is a condition you can work around. If your hearing is fluctuating and changing constantly, you won't be a good candidate for hearing devices, initially. However, once hearing fluctuations stabilize, it's good news. You don't have to live with a hearing disability. You can now invest in a hearing aid. Miniature hearing devices are available in a range of customized fittings and colors. My virtually undetected computerized device has made a huge difference in my hearing world. With computerization, you can often attain normal hearing levels, and resolve most hearing limitations.

The Well-Being Scale

If you think you're feel bad, well, the news is you are right! The quality of life factor for Meniere's sufferers has been tested and quantified by research. The 'Quality of Well-Being' scale compares Meniere's disease to extremely ill adults with a life-threatening illness such as Cancer or Aids, and that's when you're not having acute episodes of rotational vertigo.

When having acute attacks, your quality of well-being is close to a non-institutionalized Alzheimer's patient, an Aids victim, or a Cancer patient — six days before death. The research quantifies that Meniere's sufferers lost 43.9% from the optimum well-being position of ordinary people. Meniere's sufferers are the most severely impaired non-hospitalized patients studied so far. This score reflects significant impairment in mobility, physical activity, social activity, and clear thinking patterns.

Meniere's patients are in the significantly depressed category. This information puts experiences of depression, mobility, social difficulties, and clear thinking into perspective. Despite all of this, maybe it's time to keep Meniere's disease in perspective. It is NOT terminal. If you have Meniere's, you get the wonderful opportunity to work on your quality of life. Often, people who suffer from the long-term chronic condition of Meniere's, lose touch with the possibilities of their potential, restrict activities, won't try new things and become fearful of extending limits. Fear makes cowards of us all.

Adaptation is so important in moving on with life. Go out and enjoy yourself! The time between diagnosis and full recovery should not be a waste of time. Do what you can do. Push through perceived barriers and get a larger life. I never imagined I would be able to surf, learn to snow ski and snowboard, windsurf, and do intensive weight training while I had Meniere's. Everything is possible. When you set your mind on a goal, it's amazing how your body goes along with your decision. The more you do, the more you can do.

After being diagnosed with Meniere's, I was standing at one of life's crossroads. It seemed to me the decision was to wear slippers, or put on running shoes. I chose all-terrain walking shoes.

I had to make a definite decision to not let this disease dominate. When you don't have any guidelines, it becomes very overwhelming and challenging. You can't stand still to wait for something to make a difference. You must quietly, slowly, and steadily do a range of physical activities that require effort and focused balance.

If you want to extend yourself, just look for ways around a limitation until there is no limitation. Get out of bed and into life. Do a little more each day. Try something you have never done before. Stay focused, with purpose. Always extend yourself by increments. Listen to your body, and don't be afraid to try. Every simple thing you do will make a difference. Be prepared for setbacks. But don't give up on your goals for health and recovery. Make the decision to not let this condition dominate your life.

Cognitive Issues

Research substantiates that cognitive ability in vestibular sufferers is decreased. Here is a list of the key elements that are being researched on Cognitive disturbances in vestibular patients.

The first finding: A decreased ability to track two processes at once. Something well people take for granted. If you have two different things you want to do at the same time, you will have conflicting emotions and ensuing confusion. You may also find it very difficult to express this confusion.

The second finding: Trouble tracking the flow of a normal conversation or the sequence of events in a story or article.

The third finding: Decreased mental stamina.

The fourth finding: Decreased memory retrieval ability. The inability to retrieve information reliably from long term memory.

The fifth finding: Decreased sense of inner certainty. When situations need action, you have difficulty feeling confident about making a decision, even over small issues.

The sixth finding: Decreased ability to grasp the whole concept.

When I developed Meniere's disease, I noticed the first change in my attitude was frustration and anger over other people's demands. The people weren't the problem, it was the fact of having to cope with multiple demands, one after the other.

Handling more than one issue at a time became hard. It was increasingly difficult to determine priorities. In a multiple demand situation, this became very obvious to me. I was even having trouble recalling details from the previous day. I started losing that sense of rightness. You know that feeling where you are sure it's right, and you can act on that sureness. I would lose the plot in an intense conversation. Talking became tiring, especially if there was more than one subject being discussed. While these changes are happening, you don't think anyone else notices. Family, friends, and work colleagues will definitely see a change. They may not understand exactly how it is for you, but they will react. So this is the time to disclose your condition, if you haven't already.

Meniere
Circles

When you have been on top of your life game, Meniere's suddenly makes your life unpredictable. It's a shock to find that you can't even accomplish the smallest things when you want to. This takes away your self-confidence. When you are trying to cope with these dynamics, you naturally practice forms of self-protection. You start living within small proven safe patterns. I call them safety circles. These circles become smaller and smaller as you become less and less confident. Over time, it becomes challenging to step outside of even the smallest circle.

What you must do, if you have not done so already, is to expand your social and physical parameters, little by little. Expand the dynamic of you. When you are confident, look at the wider circle you have created and start expanding those new parameters. Believe is a great motto. Believe in your ability to achieve a walk around the park. Believe you can have more energy if you build up your health. Or that you can achieve anything you set your mind to. When you believe in yourself, you move towards mental and physical health.

Right now, you are in a fantastic position to take advantage of what life has to offer. New skills. New Ideas. New personal power. That's why you shouldn't put your life on hold.

Burning Out

Many sufferers find that vertigo symptoms subside and reduce significantly after several years, usually four to seven. Their hearing loss stabilizes at a moderate to severe level. This burning-out occurs in many patients. But unfortunately, this is not the case for everyone. The burning-out doesn't mean Meniere's has gone; it can make an appearance later. Burning-out means the hearing in the affected ear has been permanently destroyed, and the attacks are less intense or have stopped.

The risk of developing the disease in the opposite ear is estimated to be as high as thirty percent. Most doctors believe that if you are going to suffer bilateral Meniere's, the symptoms usually occur in the unaffected ear within two to five years. However, as with most of Meniere's research, these numbers are not agreed upon by everyone.

The thought of being affected in both ears is disconcerting, and I can't say never crossed my mind. Still, I didn't dwell on the lottery of that probability. I believe that if you get as healthy as you can and avoid stress, you give yourself a better chance of avoiding the bilateral outcome.

Even today, I apply most everything I have written in this book. I follow my own advice. I also caution my adult children on the dangers of overworking, and stressing out.

Meniere's Management

There are ways to manage your symptoms and still do the things you want to do. Nothing is standing in your way except your attitude towards your illness. Allow your spirit to rise above what may appear to be a condition with insurmountable obstacles. You're the one who can do this by consistent and determined actions.

Meniere's is an extremely confrontational condition. The critical point to remember is this, Meniere's is not terminal. Regardless of how uncomfortable or difficult it is now, you have an opportunity to get better, recover fully and live life you again.

I have a good friend Jeff who is an outdoor survival expert. He says, in a desperate situation, the most significant survival technique is to maintain a daily routine. Meniere's creates chaos, that's why you need to set up a daily routine.

This is not an excuse to set up a comfortable pattern and live in it forever. You must set up a healthy regular routine to achieve a wellness objective. Then keep adding to it to meet another set of health objectives.

One target could be reducing salt. Once you have achieved cutting down the salt, go on and add in a new regime. This could be as simple as taking a daily vitamin. Keep taking away the negative and adding the positive. You'll create a healthy pattern of achievement. Everything you do will have a positive effect. Remember it takes about four months to form a new habit. The more you can do, the closer you come to putting Meniere symptoms behind you.

Get Physical

The first objective I decided on was to keep physically fit. My routine was to walk four streetlights every morning, regardless of how I felt. Over the weeks, this turned into a gentle twenty-minute walk. There were times when I thought I wouldn't make it back home. At other times I felt good and so pleased to be out and going forward, rather than staying in the house.

Create a physical routine. Start by setting a small walking goal. It can be as simple as walking down the road for ten streetlights. Then set another goal that you are sure you can achieve easily. In time you will look back and realize you are doing things you never thought possible. Once you achieve one exercise goal, set another. Goal setting is essential. It doesn't matter how small the goal is, as long as you reach it.

Exercise yourself to wellness. Don't let the sensation of tinnitus, unsteadiness, or tiredness, get you down. Push yourself gently, and keep monitoring your response. Don't give over to fear and lethargy. It is too easy to not do anything to feel safe and secure. As soon as an attack is over, get up, get on your feet, and do something like sit in the backyard, feel the air and breathe, listen to the birds. It doesn't matter how small or insignificant it is —everything you do matters.

Go ahead, extend physical boundaries, set and achieve continuous goals. It's the cornerstone for rebuilding your life.

The Iron Factor

In the beginning, I decided that being physically fit was the foundation for recovery. Physical confidence is one of the areas that is affected by Meniere's. You need to be physically strong and balanced. The benefit is the return of self-confidence.

I started to go to the gym regularly. I talked to athletes about setting fitness objectives, how to recover quickly from workouts, and build stamina. This constant process of building strength meant understanding how to effect change in the body. This principle interested me as I wanted to rebuild a healthy body. I decided see what the gym could do for Meniere Man. I had nothing to lose and everything to gain.

I started with light weights, and over time, I added small weight increments to my routine. Working your muscles to the point of muscle exhaustion is the objective. Work to failure and be congratulated for a job well done. Rest for thirty seconds and begin again. It is really fascinating to feel your body recover in thirty seconds. I researched and applied the same recovery nutrition principles I learned in the gym to help me recover quickly from vertigo attacks. After six months, my balance and overall strength had increased considerably. I had a great deal more energy and stamina.

Research on weight-bearing exercise in retirement and age-care homes shows that immediate benefits are obtained with light weight-bearing exercise. In a short time, the elderly who exercise with weights, get more robust and more independent. They don't fall over as much, and are far more active.

The benefits of weight- bearing exercise are too many to ignore. There is no age, gender, or level of illness that should stop you from getting the benefits by doing gentle, regular weight-bearing exercise. Weight training improves blood pressure, muscular strength, bone density, and your nervous system. Plus, the psychological benefit of personal confidence and self-esteem. Weight training creates a balanced body. This helps your body counter and compensate for any unsteadiness from the effects of Meniere's.

Don't be put off by the word gym. Make an effort to leave the house to exercise. When you have a window of time, take the opportunity. Go to the gym specifically to workout. To work on individual muscle groups with real intensity. The aim is to pay attention within each moment, and focus intently on what you are doing. This makes the workouts far more interesting.

This intense focus made me realize how much my mind affects my ability to achieve goals. A negative thought, while lifting at your maximum, meant failure in the lift. A positive thought, with the same weight, meant a successful lift. The mind experience of failure and success was obvious; you just couldn't ignore its principle. Think positively. Haven't we all heard that before? However, the experience of failing and succeeding physically made the law of positive thinking all the more potent.

The critical factor is having a measurable and quantifiable means of seeing progress. You're in control and making a considerable difference to your quality of life. The intense focus on weight- bearing exercises keeps you in the present, in the now. Intense concentration in the present creates a state where you no longer hear your tinnitus, and for moments you don't register the symptoms.

My gym training wasn't all success, though! I made errors of judgment. There were times when I did too much exercise, got overtired, and had an increase in Meniere's attacks. Learn to pay attention to the signals your body gives you. Take a rest. Drink plenty of water. Sit quietly for and let your body recover. Respect what your body tells you. Work with a nutritionist and a weight program designed for you. Don't forget to inform them of your condition. A gym will design a specific program for you. Ask about a core balance program. In some gyms, individually tailored fitness plans are free with membership. The first four months of any gym membership is where the likelihood of dropping out happens. Your muscles get sore, and it can be hard to find the motivation to go. I did improve my strength three times over, and my body was equally strong on both sides. I took up windsurfing and skiing. So, not too bad for a Meniere's guy who thought that a twenty-minute walk, nine months before, was beyond him.

People say gyms are expensive but if you have given up drinking, or smoking, then do the healthy math! Many gyms' offer free consultations with personal trainers who can help you set a program. Whether you have a trainer to monitor your progress at every session, or every six weeks, you will benefit from their expertise and discipline. They offer inspiration and motivation. Knowing your trainer is at the gym waiting for you, means you're less likely to cancel out. Trainers help you get results. Other options for regular workouts are joining fitness classes taken by an instructor in a local community center, joining a gym (they often have special deals), or following a regular fitness program on the TV.

Balance Training

My next trainer had an interest in physical rehabilitation. He followed a style of training created by a man called Paul Chek, an American trainer who was responsible for looking after the top gridiron athletes in the USA. The gridiron teams would send injured players to Paul Chek with the knowledge that he would have them back out on the field, faster and fitter than anyone else in the rehab business. He created a rehabilitation system based on core balance training. He believed that the key to physical performance was based on strengthening the human core.

If your body is not stable in its core muscle function, any imbalance will be more pronounced. As you know, your vestibular system is affected by Meniere's, so you need to ensure your body balance receptors are strongly developed. Correct body posture and specific identification with your body's infrastructure will help compensate your imbalance issues. Bad body posture, for example, will be telling your brain you are imbalanced, which makes you feel unsteady. To give your body good balance, you need isometric training to improve your body posture. Trainers can show you how to do specific exercises to achieve this. Core training is now well recognized as essential for optimal bio-mechanics. You can find these same principles in other exercise programs, such as Pilates and yoga. Once you learn a routine, you won't need continual sessions with a trainer. You just need someone trained to show you initially, then you can practice on a ball at home.

If you combine isometric training with core muscle training, you will be able to achieve body balance, to a very high degree. You can get to the point of being able to stand perfectly still on the top of a large round exercise ball! The benefits of training will show up in your body, regardless of age or gender. You'll feel healthier and way more vital.

All knowledge gained by trainers will assist you years later. I still use the information in simple physical activities such as how to pick objects up off the floor by bending your knees and contracting your stomach muscles to support the back. Once you've been shown how to stand evenly and in balance, protecting and strengthening your back is something you'll do quite naturally.

With your body balanced and strong, every cell of your body, including the inner ear, will benefit. A healthy fit body can heal more quickly. Physical training enables your body to recover its balance faster after attacks. You will really start to feel the difference in your health.

If you liked sports, or exercise before you were diagnosed with Meniere's, don't stop. The importance of stimulating the sensory body through physical activity will help you improve your balance and recovery. Medical researchers are finding that intense exercise within the first six months of an injury or onset of a condition, gives patients a higher expectation of recovering from physical losses. I believe this is true with Meniere's disease.

At the start, I was having trouble picking up a ball and throwing it to my daughter without feeling dizzy. Then one year later, after exercising in the form I have described, I was going windsurfing with her regularly. Without core balance training, I would never have gone out on the water in strong winds to give it a go.

I have gained so many benefits from exercise that I urge you to do the same. Don't wait until you feel better to start. Understand that you won't feel great to begin with, so be patience with yourself. You may feel dizzy during a workout, or have a vertigo attack after. So resist the urge to blame physical activity for feeling unwell. Chances are, you would feel the same whether you were working out or lying in front of the TV.

Building strength, gaining body balance, is the proper way forward. You'll not only feel better. You'll look younger, fitter, and stronger.

Vitamin Power

One day I heard a doctor talking on a radio program, about how every illness and condition is caused by a lack of minerals and/or vitamins. Since we can't get all nutrients from foods, he recommended vitamin and mineral supplements.

The gist of what he said made sense to me. I started reading up on vitamins, their role and benefits to the body. The more you understand the importance of how specific minerals and vitamins affect your well-being, the more you'll be able to help yourself to obtain maximum health.

I found out that stress depletes the adrenal glands. So I started taking vitamins to support the adrenal glands. I was determined to step up my physical goals and improve my health.

To trial the effect of additional vitamins, I chose the most common ailment: the common cold, a sure sign of a weak immune system. I decided to see whether I could work out a vitamin regime that would give me a noticeable result. No more colds or flu would be my goal.

I decided to support my immune system by taking high levels of Vitamin C as a winter booster. I started taking 1000cc of Vitamin C a day. The following month, I gradually increased the dosage to 4000cc a day. During the cold season, I experienced a high immunity to colds. That winter, the family came down with respiratory ailments but I didn't. I was the one bringing them boxes of tissues and hot lemon honey drinks. During that winter my daughter caught the flu and was in bed for five days, then my son, then my wife. I had Meniere's but no flu. This pattern was repeated often during the winters. I can only recall getting a mild cold and flu once. When the winter snow thawed, I would cut the dose back to 1000 cc of Vitamin C daily.

I looked into what I could do to help myself with Meniere's disease. I found that complex vitamin B assists with nerve regeneration, reducing stress, depression, and picking up energy levels. Essential Fatty Acids reduce inflammation and help nerve transmission and repair cell membranes. Essential Fatty Acids come from fatty fish like salmon, and vegetable oils. As well as eating a diet rich in oily fish, I took fish oil and flax-seed oil in a supplement form three times a day. Also, a multi-vitamin once a day.

In time my vitamin drawer was often a source of humor for my friends because of the assortment of vitamins there. But I was on a mission. I knew that vitamin supplements along with a healthy diet made all the difference to my recovery from Meniere's.

My daily vitamin regime included the following supplements. But with all supplements, check with your health professional first.

Vitamin B Complex: assists the nervous system. Reduces stress, depression, and picks up energy levels. Supports the immune system.

Vitamin E: Promotes healing; 24 mg spread throughout the day at meals.

Essential Fatty Acids: regenerates cell membranes, reduce inflammation and assist in nerve cell transmission. Fish oil liquid or capsules 1000 mg 3 times a day. Flaxseed oil 5 ml 3 times a day. (Use as a dressing for salads, but do not heat the oil and cook with it).

Vitamin C: supports the kidneys, liver, and immune system. 2000-4000 cc spread throughout the day and at least one hour before or after food. I take up to 4000 cc a day if I am feeling like I am getting a cold, but usually I take 1000 cc daily to keep my immune system supported.

Multi-vitamin: One a day. My choices are Swisse Men/Women Ultivite or TwinLab. These brands have documented high- quality sources.

Additional Supplements

If you are going through a particularly stressful time, take vitamins to specifically support your adrenal glands and immune system. Calcium, zinc, niacin, oil of primrose, borage oil, selenium, magnesium, l-carnitine, chromium, co-enzyme Q10, and extra B6, B12.

Supplements can interact with medications, so always check with your health professional first. Don't forget to drink plenty of mineral water every day. Not tap water! Pure still water, (avoid carbonated as it has a higher salt content). Read the label and go for the lowest salt, and highest magnesium. Evian spring water has a high content of magnesium.

Eat. Drink. Play.

The inner ear, when healthy, has an independent regulatory fluid system and is not affected by any chemical or the blood fluid volume dynamics of the body's fluid system.

Meniere's results in the loss of the independent fluid function of the inner ear. The damage from attacks means the fluid system of the inner ear is no longer independent from the rest of the body. This results in the fluid volume and chemical concentration of the inner ear being subject to the chemical make up of the body's blood fluid. Any fluctuation of the body's blood/fluid volume and chemical makeup can cause symptoms in the ear, such as the sensation of fullness, pressure, and tinnitus. It can also give you dizziness and imbalance. This does not mean an attack is imminent, these are other symptoms that you may experience.

You are what you eat. And drink! The vitamins, minerals, and water you put in your body matter to your Meniere's recovery. Eating is one of life's great pleasures, and you can keep enjoying food. However, you won't be able to indulge in salty foods because salt is one of the main elements linked to vertigo attacks. So let's look at why salt is the bad boy in food.

The inner ear is bathed in a precise concentration of sodium and potassium. If you alter this delicate balance by eating food high in salt (sodium), which in turn is absorbed into your bloodstream, you set yourself up for a fast delivery of high concentrated sodium solution immediately into the defenseless inner ear. This results in an imbalance of sodium and potassium concentration. The inner ear desperately tries to even out these sodium concentration levels by diluting the chamber, with water. The chamber with the highest concentration of sodium gets the most water. This, in turn, expands one of the compartments. As a result, the separating Reissner's membrane becomes so extended, that it ruptures and floods the vestibular system. The result is a vertigo attack.

This is why you must limit salt intake to around 1000 mg or less a day. This level of salt represents a low salt diet. Some salt is vital for body function. So you don't want to have a zero salt diet. You just need to control the intake to around 1000 - 2000 mg a day. The body needs salt to function, so don't try to cut out all salt. Before making dietary changes, do check with your physician first.

Get to know how much salt is in raw and processed foods. How much salt you ingest in a day needs to be monitored by you. There are no salt police about! Restrict your daily salt intake or suffer the consequences.

One of the top vestibular specialists told me that he recommends that his Meniere's patients don't eat out at restaurants because they cannot control the amount of salt in the food. I disagree with this. You need to get out and enjoy life as everyone else does. Don't stop eating out for fear of eating the wrong thing and aggravating Meniere's. Don't stop participating in social occasions. It is imperative to keep up social contact, don't fall into a reclusive style of living.

Restaurant food is about choice. Look at your favorite restaurant menus and make your dietary decisions, based on the salt content. Here's my advice on eating out.

Italian Food: Look for meals that don't have sauces on them. Try the fish or veal without sauces or ask for sauces on the side.

Fast Food: All fast foods are out. They all have way to much salt added to the crumbs, batters, sauces, and dressings.

Japanese: A terrific way of eating. The sashimi, nigiri, and tempura are good sources of food with low salt. Salads are also good.

Don't eat the shabu-shabu as the stock base is salted. Miso soup is heavy in added salt. Stay away from seaweed soups and sauces. Wasabi (hot green horseradish paste) in the sushi is my only vice, and as a result, I suffer from increased tinnitus.

Japanese is my food of choice. And by the way, most restaurant now have low-salt soy. Check it out, or ask for it. Sushi without soy sauce takes a little getting used to. Instead of using soy, you can dip food in mirin, a fermented rice wine, which tastes delicious.

Alcohol: Minimize beer and wine to a glass. I have found that spirits are out, as spirits, and liqueurs seem to increase tinnitus and my hearing drops significantly. I suspect it's because the high alcohol content raises your blood pressure, which will affect your inner ear system.

French Cuisine: Sauces feature heavily in French regional dishes. Pick simple dishes without sauces. Salt is a major taste ingredient for sauces in particular. Even butter contains salt.

Korean: The dishes cooked in the restaurant kitchen are full of spices and salt. But if you order food and cook it yourself at the table, in the traditional manner, then you are in control of all the ingredients in your meal. All the meat, vegetables, and spices, come on separate plates. It's a fun way to eat with friends. Forget the spices and you'll be OK. Again don't go for anything that has sauces or has been pre-cooked.

Chinese: It's often loaded with msg (monosodium glutamate) and table salt. Steamed Dim Sums are great, if they don't contain msg or salt. There are Chinese restaurants that don't use msg or much salt.

Indian food Now this is unfortunate as I can't think of an Indian dish that does not have a sauce containing salt. I now only eat Indian curries at home. I make them myself, no salt, and a limited amount of mild or medium strength curry powder. Don't use curry paste as this is often very high in salt. You can make an excellent curry without salt by using limes, ginger, lemon-grass, garlic, shallots, turmeric, cumin, and pepper.

Cafes: If you're an urban person, this is a stimulating environment, but if you're a Meniere's sufferer, drinking caffeinated coffee is an issue. But, you can have your cake and coffee too. If you drink decaffeinated coffee, you can enjoy the social benefits of cafe life without aggravating Meniere symptoms.

If you apply a few simple rules of healthy living, your overall health will be greater and your Meniere's symptoms less. Limit alcohol. Eat a low salt diet. Eat complex carbohydrates, which give greater long-term energy for your body.

Sugars in processed foods cause sudden sugar spikes that you want to avoid. People with Meniere's are sugar sensitive. You will notice that sugar negatively affects your body. I found that even a teaspoon of sugar added to my coffee or sprinkled on cereal, affected my hearing immediately and caused an increase in tinnitus.

Cut out simple sugars like soft drinks, candy, sweets, jams, and cakes, as they are absorbed into your bloodstream quickly. This is really important. Eat complex carbohydrates rather than refined sugars.

Take note of hidden sugars. Packaged goods have the sugar content writing on the back or side of the product. Note also that some low-fat foods contain more sugar to add taste. So get into a habit of reading the labels on products and comparing brands.

Think of having a low salt and low sugar diet, not in terms of restrictions, but rather for optimal health. Less salt means less issues with blood pressure, hypertension, and strokes. Low sugar means less risk of coronary disease, diabetes, and better weight management. Reduced sugar, and salt means you lower the risk for most major health issues.

In the early stages of Meniere's disease, I cut down on spicy foods. I was made aware of my body's reaction to foods and additives through increased tinnitus levels. Hot-spices like Bombay curry powder, increase the blood volume in your body, which affects the fluid pressure in your inner ear. Cutting out spicy foods is not a permanent measure. Later you will be able to eat a bowl of chilies! But while in the acute stages of the disease, when you are prone to vertigo attacks, I would leave the chili out. Replace for taste: Herbs for spices. Your meals don't need to be bland and tasteless. There is a garden of herbs to give food a piquant taste, like parsley, basil, coriander, mint, chervil, marjoram.

Look for foods that are primary products such as vegetables, whole grains and fresh protein. Try to cut out or limit down foods that come in a tin or packet. Avoid ready-cooked or processed foods like spaghetti sauce in a jar or dried soup in packets. Read the labels and pick the lowest sodium content.

Meals should consist of protein, complex carbohydrates with no wasted calories from refined sugars, and processed foods. Fresh vegetables, fish, chicken, meat, fruit grain cereals, and breads are smart choices.

Another huge factor in promoting health is giving up smoking. You can't afford to light up, because smoking restricts blood vessels. This affects the ability of blood to circulate efficiently in the inner ear. Limiting blood supply to anywhere in your body is a problem. Your ear needs the healing substances which are carried in your blood. If your ear doesn't get what it needs, it's in a vulnerable state and more likely to be prone to ongoing Meniere's trouble. Make sure your body gets as much healthy blood circulation as possible.

Your body is continually renewing itself. So make sure you take the opportunity to rebuild yourself to be stronger, and better than ever before. If you are a smoker, and have Meniere's disease, stop smoking.

Maintain your blood sugar levels by making sure you eat a balanced breakfast of protein and complex carbohydrates. Don't skip meals during the day or leave long gaps without eating. Think in terms of six small meals instead of the traditional three big meals a day. Eating a big meal will spike your blood sugar levels, causing feelings of tiredness, lethargy and even depression. So remember to keep your body fueled up.

Environmental Equations

While figuring out the management of Meniere's, I went back to nature. I found water especially therapeutic. Relaxing in the pool. Standing under a shower. Swimming in the ocean, or sitting near a lake or a river. The benefits of mountain and sea are universally acknowledged through civilizations as places of rejuvenation.

Rather like the old methods of cures, where the sick were ordered to take rest in the mountains or by the sea, I also discovered the benefits of mountain air at high altitude. How taking family time together, away from the city, the air crisp and skies blue, rejuvenated body and soul.

I wondered why getting away from the city made me feel so much better. Scientific research demonstrates that the content of Ion in the air is of great importance to air quality. People living in forests, near waterfalls, and the seashore enjoy much better quality air and freshness. This is because the Ion content in these places is 1000 times more than office buildings and urban residential areas.

The oxygen combined with Ion is active and easily absorbed by human organs, which benefits the body and revives the spirit. In relation to human health, a forest (or a waterfall) has 100,000 - 500,000 Ion S/CC per milliliter, aiding spontaneous recovery. Mountain and seashore have 50.000 - 100,000 Ion S/CC and fields 5,000 - 50,000, enhancing immunity. Compared with enclosed urban and residential areas 40 - 50 Ion S/CC, are known to induce psychological disorders, headaches, and insomnia. Does a negative environment, polluted and crowded cities defer reaching our optimum sense of well-being, and delay our healing?

With health in mind, if you can't get to the mountains or sea occasionally, take a long shower, take a walk on wet, dewy morning grass. Stand in a warm natural outdoor shower of summer rain. Sleep in a well-ventilated room. Consider purchasing houseplants, or a remote controller air cooler/humidifier with an ionizing feature to create a healthier environment.

Alternative Therapies

In the process of getting better, I formulated a vitamin regime, a fitness plan, and changed my diet. I had come along way in my personal self-management program. However, I was still a little frustrated by not being able to do more than one intense activity a day. I was pleased with the progress in training and my health so far. But I still wanted to be able to do more to try to reduce down the vertigo attacks and eventually be symptom-free. My ultimate goal was to overcome this disease. So I looked into alternative therapies, which I will outline here.

Acupuncture

The personal trainer I was working with went to an acupuncturist whom he highly recommended. A Chinese doctor, now in his sixties, who had once been a child athlete chosen for the Chinese international acrobatic team. He trained and performed around the world from five years of age until he was twenty-one. He later went to medical school in Shanghai. And eventually swam to Hong Kong and then later immigrated to Australia. He sounded like an interesting person to meet at the very least. So I did.

I always remember this. The old linoleum covered floor of the corridor led to a glass-paneled door. As I entered, a brass bell rang. The front room of his office was stocked with Chinese medicinal herbs in glass cabinets. Large glass jars sat on the counter full of herbs and fungi. A laminated acupuncturist's chart hung on the wall. Energy flow lines were illustrated running around the body like electrical wiring, little red, black, and yellow dots indicating electrical junction points, areas for precise needlework. Acupuncture is an ancient Chinese practice for tuning the body's energy fields and is widely recognized in the west as a legitimate form of medicine.

The acupuncturist was very enthusiastic

and skilled. As I got to know him better, he showed me his acrobatic maneuvers, which he learned as a child in China. One of them was a handstand on a rotating, rolling office chair. He stayed that way for about five minutes. Talking to me about China with his hands gripped around the armrests of his chair and suspended upside down, perfectly still, except for the trousers that slid down from his ankles, exposing his white socks and black shoes. As he came down, he said, "I'll always be able to do that, it doesn't matter how old."

I began to trust this man, and we went into the more advanced stages of acupuncture. "You can do this." He told me I was able to withstand pain and would benefit from having more, with intensity. "I have looked up your Meniere's in my journals. This moxibustion would be very beneficial for you. It will help this Meniere's." So my initiation into the Chinese healing art of moxibustion began.

"Sit very still. When the pain gets to six out of ten, let me know. If you can get to eight or nine, that would be even better. I'll just cut your hair a little bit here at the top of your head." Then he put something on top of my head and lit it. I sat very still. Soon I smelt incense, not perfumed incense, but a medicinal, resinous, herbal fragrance.

I waited. Nothing. No pain. Then, a little tingling on the top of my head, then the pain came! At first, I counted the pain level as a four. Then the unnerving burning sensation fixed solidly in my skull bone. Where was he? He had this uncanny ability to disappear at crucial, excruciating moments. It was a mortal relief when he finally extinguished the moxi fire. The pain slowly lifted. He said moxibustion is very good. I burned a special Chinese herb on your head. He laughed. I returned for more sessions.

Several months later, I was at home, looking at the top of my head with a mirror. I had a dark red burn the size of a quarter. I gingerly felt it, and to my horror, it moved a little. When the scab came off, I couldn't believe it. I had a hole in my head shaped like China. An area of my scalp had been burnt down to the bone. I didn't go back for further moxi treatments!

Despite the scar on my scalp, I felt so much better from all the treatments. The acupuncture sessions were a turning point for me. Even after I had stopped the sessions, I still had positive benefits from acupuncture. My attacks became less frequent and far less distressing. The acupuncture treatment raised my energy levels up and my skin color and tone were healthier looking. I looked, and felt much healthier.

I do believe the acupuncturist cared about my health and did his utmost to help me. But the extra moxi hole in the head, and the promise of curing my baldness, went a bit overboard! Now, I wear a cap, or a hat, in every photo!

I have read since that the head is the one place where a practitioner should not burn moxi cones. If you decide to go this route, a registered acupuncturist will advise you on treatment methods and options. I really recommend acupuncture for general health.

Hypnotherapy

Hypnotherapy was my next adventure into Meniere relief. I was recommended to a therapist, who unlocked childhood traumas. These forgotten child dramas apparently create major problems in your adult life. Releasing these blocks through therapy can greatly assist adult healing.

I was on the healing journey, so along I went. I thought maybe my childhood was dramatic enough to have caused some blockages. Perhaps I've been blocked since childhood, and now in later life, Meniere's is the result. I had no idea, but neither do the best medical researchers in the world. Still, I found myself counting backward, then recounting events from childhood. Hypnotherapy didn't make any difference to me. But as the saying goes, different strokes for different folks.

Cranial Manipulation

There is a gentle art of cranial manipulation. I asked around and found a practitioner who was almost impossible to get an appointment with. He was getting good results with all sorts of patients. A month later, my appointment time arrived. I was full of expectation and hope. I walked into his office, but he was a she, as he had gone on sabbatical.

I lay down, and she applied very light and sensitive pressure on my head, using the palms of her hands. In this way, she 'read' my skull. She accurately identified an old but significant trauma to my skull that I had happened to me. She said it was probably a major accident as the impact must have been severe. And my neck was out of alignment and perhaps had been for a while.

I was impressed with the diagnosis and subtle manipulation. I left an hour later. I went back three times, but I didn't notice any real change to my condition. Some people persevere with cranial manipulation and claim noticeable results.

Massage

If you decide on having a course of massage therapy, it's essential to only have gentle massages. Deep tissue sports massage can be stressful on a physical level. The key to preventing issues is to stipulate what you don't want. You don't want neck manipulation of any description. Gentle massage is excellent. As your shoulders, back, and neck muscles will be tense from the continual adjustments your body makes for balance.

I went for regular full body massage sessions with great results. Any imbalance in my muscles was corrected. I slept better, was less tired, and I had an overall sense of well-being.

My masseur was a young man who had literally fought his way back from the dead. I heard his intriguing personal story over many massages. His story was of a motorbike accident in his teens —a traumatic event which left him in a coma for two months. He was expected to have extensive brain damage as his skull was severely crushed. When he woke up, he had a large metal plate in his head. Then, rehabilitation and after two months sent home to be a living but mobile vegetable. He refused to accept his physical and social restrictions. So six months later, he booked a flight overseas, paying for tickets with some of his accident compensation money. His plan was to survive alone, away from his doctor's and family's restrictive prognosis and care.

Two years later, he arrived back home, having traveled the world, living on his instincts and very little money. He most definitely was not a vegetable as doctors had predicted. He had gained a black belt in combat martial art. And now, here he was. Five years after his accident, living with a beautiful girl in his own house. He was massaging for a living while studying to be an osteopath. Despite the odds stacked against him, he was living a spectacular life.

His complete dedication and belief in his ability to affect recovery was a poignant lesson for me. And he was very entertaining with a great sense of humor. It is fascinating how many inspirational stories come from everyday people overcoming incredible obstacles. One day, while I was having a massage and talking through the hole in the table, his little pet rabbit hopped under the massage table. A white rabbit with bright red eyes, like glass marbles that only rabbits have.

"What made you get a rabbit for a pet?" I asked."Well, I do kids magic shows on weekends. I am a clown, and I do magic tricks with the rabbit. But I've stopped doing it because I don't particularly like children. Way too noisy and active!" He went on to say that to conquer his fear of timidity, he took up flame blowing. "You mean where you take a flammable liquid in your mouth and light it as you blow out?" I asked. "Yeah, that's the one. Someone at the last party put the wrong propellant in the container, and it burned too soon, so I scorched my face and arm." I thought his face looked a little red but hadn't thought that much about it. "Only did it three weeks ago. I visualized my face and arm healing every two hours," he said. Later, when I turned over and had a close look at him, it was remarkable. He had a photo of the burns soon after the accident. The recovery was surprising, considering the small time frame. The masseur magician had revealed his secret for recovery. To overcome obstacles, you must believe in the power of positive visualization. He also believes in creating his reality and constantly extending himself. So do I.

Biofeedback

When I was first diagnosed, a psychologist recommended biofeedback monitoring, which help you train the parts of your body that you have control over. For example, your thoughts, your ability to relax your muscles.

Sitting in a chair, I was connected to a machine by a series of electrodes. I felt no pain or sensations during this monitoring. I was asked to close my eyes and visualize the figure 1: breathing in to the count of three, and out to the count of three. Thirty minutes later, the psychologist explained what levels of relaxation I had obtained, and the length of time I was the most deeply relaxed.

Over six weeks, I soon became familiar with different levels of relaxation. This method of monitored meditation enabled me to quantify the depth and length of relaxation.

At home, I practiced the same meditation method. Practicing with biofeedback made me aware of relaxation levels. I took every opportunity to relax. Waiting at the doctor's, sitting in the park, waiting for a friend. Before I experienced biofeedback, I thought that sleeping was the only time my body was rejuvenated. Now I know I can revive my energy levels through deep relaxation. I found it very beneficial as a tool for reducing stress levels.

Meditation

Stress is a significant factor in Meniere's and in modern life. I have found meditation an essential tool for coping with both anxiety and Meniere's. Meditation is deeply calming but you must practice regularly. As soon as I felt I was improving, I'd get busier and forget to do meditation. This is common. As soon as you start to feel better, you tend to forget about what made you better. So you re-instate the meditation disciplines again. Human nature, I suppose.

But the idea is to make meditation an integral part of your daily habit. You need a method of meditation practice that you can do every day, without going to an ashram.

I was keen to find some method that I could do conveniently and privately at home. Then by happenstance, I was having my skin looked at microscopically by my skin specialist. I was talking to him about the relaxation method called biofeedback and asked whether he had heard of it."Yes." A man of few words, but a keen eye. He told me he had another form of meditation that he had been practicing regularly.

He gave me a meditation program made up of a series of CDs that you progress through over months. The starter set sounded like ocean waves rolling onto the sand, while a deep sounding voice-over guided you through the meditation.

During the meditation sessions, my tinnitus was completely masked. The CDs gave me one hour that was just for meditation. After spending an hour meditating, I was alert, and my energy level restored and I felt refreshed.

The benefits I received from meditation were less stress, less tinnitus, a positive life perspective, increased energy levels, hopefulness, and a sense of oneness with life. All this and the luxury of having a quiet time to myself, meditation became a breeze. I could put on a CD every day, at whatever hour I decided, and all the family left me alone. I was totally blissed out. Meditation became a sanctuary I escaped to everyday. The relief of not focusing on Meniere's is a gift worth giving yourself. An hour a day of meditation will put your life into perspective, guaranteed. I highly recommend meditation as part of your de-stress program.

At the time of writing, I am re-reading a book called *Full Catastrophe Living* by Jon Kabat-Zinn. It's a book about how to cope with stress, pain, and illness using mindful meditation. Jon is a Professor of Medicine emeritus at the University of Massachusetts Medical School. His book is straight forward and practical. I still use his meditation CDs daily. Jon also inspired me to record a thirty-minute guided meditation CD, specifically to help Meniere sufferers, as a companion to the book, *Let's Get Better*. I am forever grateful to Jon Kabat-Zinn for writing and giving his positive healing grace to people who need help.

A Strategy For Wellness

There comes a time when you must break out of your old habits. Early on in my personal history of Meniere's, I caught myself rushing around the car to put gas in the tank as though it was an emergency. The only thing waiting for me on the other side of the car was a fuel cap. Getting into the car and putting the key in the ignition was all done in the most efficient manner. My whole being was a study in time efficiency. And it didn't stop in the gas station it happened at home.

I wondered why I was so rushed. Then it occurred to me. I did everything in a hurry. There was no differentiation between any activities. They were all top priority in my mind. When talking with a colleague or friend, I was always impatient. I wanted to quickly finish every conversation. I was wired, and life was exhilarating.

It wasn't until sometime later that I realized

this constant activity was contributing to my attacks. This meant if I wanted to limit my attacks, I had to change my old patterns. This made me stop and look at everything I did — to identify what was contributing to my stress. The gas station rush was just one of the crazy revelations in my daily activities.

So, become aware of yourself, look at things you are doing in your life. You may have habits and patterns you got away with before, but now you have Meniere's, they will be your stress factors, which can add up to vertigo triggers.

Look at how you drive your car, eat your food, and talk to friends and family. Do you take your time, or is it all in a rush and never-ending. Only you know. Adopt a new strategy of personal awareness. You'll need to do a mental, and emotional re-evaluation. You need to re-invent your personal operating manual for day-to-day relations with friends, family, business colleagues and yourself.

If you need professional stress management help, then get it. You may decide to work with a psychologist to help you change patterns of thinking and behaviors. This is key to personal control. Adapt and be conscious of stress in your life. Lessen stress in the minutes of the moment. By reducing stress, and adopting a calmer approach, you will find your Meniere's attacks will lessen in intensity and duration.

However, as I discovered, making changes

means everyone around you will be affected. In relationships, we get used to automatic responses from people in certain situations and learn to rely on those responses. Whenever you change set patterns, it isn't easy, but necessary.

I made definite changes to lessen stress when I realized what a significant affect it had on Meniere's symptoms. As a consequence, I became unpredictable in my personal and business relationships. I no longer expressed extreme dissatisfaction or got involved in a conflict. No more rushing to complete tasks. Some tasks I left uncompleted and never finished. I stopped projecting linear time frames and participating in multiple tasking.

You can imagine how unsatisfactory this was in business and in personal relationships. I could no longer be relied on to complete tasks. Luckily this behavior was temporary! Soon I was pro-active in deciding what tasks I could do without impacting on my health or aggravating symptoms or those around me!

Ultimately you will need to look at just how, why, and what you are doing daily. Then change your activities to allow you to recover your health and manage Meniere's. The intention is to get over Meniere's disease and live a positive, productive, happy life, but still keep your friends!

Quiet Words

The first and most important thing you can do right now is to develop a new attitude, and a belief system. This will allow you to overcome physical, emotional and mental barriers. You must begin to change your mindset into a healthy state of being. Move forward to a positive future. To get you started, you may like to try my mantra.

I am not my disease.
I feel good about who I am.
I am healthy.

I repeated these lines every day aloud, three times a day, for about five minutes. Each time I said a line, I visualized a positive image of myself.

You need to believe in each phrase as you repeat it. You can use this mantra or create your own. Keep it short, so it's easy to remember.

Mantras really help. In the beginning, I felt

completely invaded and controlled by Meniere's. It was a real struggle to retain my identity. After doing the mantra, I began to feel more positive about myself and my situation, and I knew I would recover.

It is essential to begin as soon as possible. Believe you will not always feel this bad. You won't, and that's a promise! When you're first diagnosed with Meniere's, vertigo rules your life. All you can think about is Meniere's disease. It is vital to keep in mind that things can only get better. Much better!

Every little thing you do for yourself right now is a big step towards recovery. You are like the astronaut on the moon, covering new ground. You take a giant leap of faith. You get there, step by step. You take small, manageable steps to start. Sometimes it is easy to forget how much the smallest things matter.

Once you use the time between vertigo attacks, a lot changes, you'll cope with acute attacks better. The attacks seem less disturbing and don't last as long. The gaps between attacks will expand, until one day it happens —a month goes by without vertigo. Celebrate! You tick off six months with no dizziness. Until a year passes, and before you know it, you've recovered.

The Hi Friend

When you realign personal energy and attitudes, you'll come to understand a new term in the social order —the Hi Friend. The person you don't give out as much time and energy to as you previously did. The Hi Friend is just someone you say hi to in passing. They don't expect all the effort you think you need to give out. In fact, the simplicity of defining time is how you save time. And who you give time to. Not everyone needs your time and effort!

You come to prioritize because you no longer give your personal time and energy endlessly. You can't afford to. It's called personal conservation. When you practice conserving, you are not limiting yourself. You are just being more selective in individual output. And you become less stressed. We realize we don't have to do as much for people as we think. You don't have to make everyone like you. Don't do so much for people at the expense of yourself.

You'll realize by cutting back on giving out

your time, energy, and effort to everyone, you are not as indispensable and self-important as you once believed. It is stress-reducing, to realize our human input and output quota, to admit our limits and failings.

We become human. Not superhuman. We become human beings, not human doings. We take one step back out of the race. We bow out gracefully. Our values change. The fatness of our wallet becomes less critical as we become valuable to ourselves. We treat ourselves better. We make time for ourselves.

We allow ourselves to be who we want to be. We stop taking center stage and striving for applause. You have to take yourself to task and look at all areas of stress in your life. And change them. This takes time and never really stops.

Today, I no longer think I have to call all the shots. I am a better listener. I let others take responsibility. I am less rushed, and I consider others more. I am interested in other people's points of view and will hear them out. I notice the wind in the trees. I am less stressed.

Laugh. Love. Live.

The effect of happiness will have a great impact on your health. Laughing is a regenerative activity. It is statistically proven, people who are sick, recover quickly, and more comprehensively when they smile. Great ways to let laughter into your life are joke books and cartoons, comedy movies, anything that gives you a laugh. Always look at the funny side of life. Cut back on the dim and grim channels on TV and tune into laughter. It is the best medicine, and that is a scientifically proven fact. The more you laugh out loud, the better you feel.

Water and sunshine are healing balms. At every opportunity, soak in the bath or in the sea. Look for pleasures and pursue them. Make every little thing into a pleasure. It's part of a mindful recovery. You know the saying, if God is in the detail, well, that's where you should look.

Give yourself permission to not feel guilty about taking a little time out. It's another step towards feeling in control of your life. Try that one. It's not as easy as it sounds. You will find how stressed you are when you think relaxation is negative. We have so much guilt attached to not working. We inherently see it as being lazy. Go ahead, take a break and enjoy it.

The other regenerative activity is love. There's a lot of research to say that our recovery and life will be far more successful if you have someone to love. Touching, feeling, getting physical with a lover, kissing, holding, and hugging. Giving and receiving physical comfort and affection is a gift. All these activities create endorphins —the feel-good hormones in our bodies. Everything we do with, and for love, creates healing in our body. If you're living alone, think about getting a pet. The love of people and animals have tremendous healing properties. The more we give love, the more we feel loved. Every hug counts!

Postscript

Meniere's was a huge learning curve. I was desperate to get better, but how? I was short of a miracle, so I took a mindful approach. I paid more attention to what I was doing in my life. I had to change my lifestyle for the better. When symptoms became a thing of the past, I discovered what this personal suffering had taught me. There is value in every life experience we go through.

No person is an island, entirely of themselves, and no sufferer should ever suffer alone. That is why I am happy to share my experience with you.

I understand Meniere's because I have experienced life with it. I also know the lack of understanding and compassion one can find within the social structure and the subsequent additional damage that situation brings to Meniere's sufferers. I experienced the negative social impact when an educated man of authority uttered the words, "Your Meniere's is a mere minor inconvenience." A typical flippant attitude of ignorance toward Meniere's disease. Until non-sufferers understand Meniere's disease, sufferers are vulnerable physically, mentally, financially, and emotionally. Seek as much genuine support as you can.

Meniere's has allowed other qualities to come forward in my life — compassion, love, and the gift of empathy. The tiny cochlea bone inside the inner ear is a symbol of how small things can be significant. *The Self-Help Book For Meniere's Disease* as the Astronaut could have said, a small step for Meniere's but a giant step for this man. If you are reading this book, I hope it is a sure and positive step forward for you too.

I hope this book and my experience inspire you to find ways to cope and recover from Meniere's. There are actually some benefits that come from suffering. You get to know your body, its limitations, and unlimited potential. For me, I have made a total recovery. Full recovery means no vertigo, no brain fog, no wooziness, no dizziness, no 'bad days', no exhaustion and no medication. No more Meniere's. Sure, I will always have some tinnitus and reduced hearing in one ear. But even hearing loss has its advantage. If there is a neighborhood party, loud music doesn't bother me. I just dream on!

One Hundred Mindful Ways To Recovery

If I can do it.
So can you.

Meniere Man

1. Buy a new journal

2. Write down goals

3. Keep track of changes

4. Write down a vitamin regime

5. Start with single vitamin

6. Try Vitamin E and Vitamin C

7. Increase or decrease the doses

8. Extra vitamins to boost your system

9. Your daily exercise routine

10. Make a plan

11. Make some goals

12. Get moving

13. Keep moving

14. Do more than you feel like doing

15. Just start walking

16. Your daily goal for walking

17. Step by step by step

18. How far can you go

19. How long are your walks

20. Increase time of walks

21. Increase duration of walks

22. Go further than before

23. Use lamp posts as markers

24. Walk in the morning

25. Walk in the evening

26. Take the stairs

27. Get fighting fit

28. Listen to your body

29. Rest and recuperate

30. Feel alive

31. Breathe the air

32. Get to the beach

33. Find a patch of sunlight

34. Take a long shower

35. Lie in the bath

36. Do more for yourself

37. Chill

38. Small things count big time

39. Keep up your daily journal

40. Spend time with friends

41. Phone someone

42. Take photographs

43. Do what you love to do

44. Look after yourself

45. Think about you

46. Focus on your needs

47. Increase fitness levels

48. Do daily exercise

49. Small steps matter

50. Enroll in a gym

51. Meet a personal trainer

52. Expand your circles

53. Increase walking

54. Increase workouts

55. Take small incremental steps

56. Increase weights

57. Your current exercise goal is

58. Reach your goal, set another

59. Get a fitness ball for home

60. Write out an eating plan

61. Try eating 6 small meals a day

62. Cook a recipe you love

63. Be unlimited

64. Throw the salt shaker away

65. Pepper not salt

66. Replace salt with herbs

67. Clean the pantry

68. Throw out salted foods

69. Clear out the fridge

70. Go shopping for low salt items

71. Plant a herb garden

72. What foods have you replaced

73. What foods have you eliminated

74. How have you reduced salt

75. Experience alternative therapies

76. Your meditation times

77. Make a healing mantra

78. Write affirmations down

79. What's working for you

80. How are you feeling

81. What do you want to change

82. Personal challenges

83. Your main triggers

84. What are your main stresses

85. What stress have you reduced

86. Have you laughed lately

87. Watch the comedy channel

88. The small stuff. Don't sweat it

89. Get a meditation CD

90. Love a lot

91. Relax. Relax. Relax

92. Wake up, and smell the flowers

93. Small steps count to recovery

94. Book in a massage

95. Go swimming

96. Take time to be in nature

97. Take up a creative activity

98. A Mindful step, is a step forward

99. Get out more

100. Believe in a full recovery

About
Meniere Man

With a smile, and a sense of humor, the Author pens himself as Meniere Man, because, as he says, Meniere's disease changed his life dramatically. At the height of his business career and aged just forty-six, he suddenly became acutely ill. He was diagnosed with Meniere's disease. He began to lose all hope that he would fully recover his health. However, the full impact of having Meniere's disease was to come later. He lost not only his health but also his career and financial status as well.

It was his personal spirit and desire to get 'back to normal' that turned his life around for the better. He decided that you can't put a limit on anything in life. Rather than letting Meniere's disease get in the way of life, he started to focus on what to do about overcoming Meniere's disease.

With the advice on healing and recovery in his books, anyone reading the advice given, can make simple changes, and find a way toward a recovery from Meniere's disease. These days life is different for the Author. He is a fit man who has no symptoms of Meniere's, except for tinnitus and hearing loss in one ear. He does not take any medication. All the physical activities he enjoys these days require a high degree of balance: snowboarding, surfing, hiking, windsurfing, and weight training. All these things, he started to do while suffering from Meniere's disease symptoms. Meniere Man believes that if you want to experience a marked improvement in health, you can't wait until you feel well to start. You must begin to improve your health immediately, even though you may not feel like it.

The Author is a writer, painter, designer, and exhibiting artist. He is married to a Poet and Essayist. They have two adult children.

He spends his time writing and painting. He loves the sea, cooking, traveling, nature, family, friends and his beloved dog, Bella.

If you enjoyed this book and think it could be helpful to others, please leave a review.

BELLA

References

American Academy of Otolaryngology-Head and Neck Surgery's 1995

Guidelines for the Diagnosis and Evaluation of Therapy in Meniere's disease.

AAO- HNS: American Academy of Otolaryngology and Head and Neck Surgery; PTA: Pure Tone Audiometry; DHI: Dizziness Handicap Inventory

American Academy of Otolaryngology-Head and Neck Foundation, Inc.(1995). 'Committee on Hearing and Equilibrium guidelines for the diagnosis and evaluation of therapy in Meniere's disease. ' Otolaryngol Head Neck Surg 113(3): 181-185.

Anderson JP, Harris JP. Impact of Meniere's disease on quality of life. Otol Neurotol 22:888-894,2001

HAVIA M, Kentala E. Progression of symptoms of dizziness in Meniere's disease. Arch Otolaryngol Head Neck Surg 2004;130:431-5.

Honrubia V. Pathophysiology of Meniere's disease. Meniere's Disease (Ed. Harris JP) 231-260, 1999, Pub: Kugler (The Hague)

Huppert, D., et al. (2010). 'Long-term course of Meniere's disease revisited.' Acta Otolaryngol 130(6): 644-651.

MATEIJSEN DJ, Van Hengel PW, Van Huffelen WM, Wit HP, Albers FW. Pure-tone and speech audiometry in patients with Meniere's disease. Clin Otolaryngol 2001; 26: 379-87.

Santos, P. M., R. A. Hall, et al. (1993). 'Diuretic and diet effect on Meniere's disease evaluated by the 1985 Committee on Hearing and Equilibrium guidelines.' Otolaryngol Head Neck Surg 109(4): 680-9.

Savastino M, Marioni G, Aita M. Psychological characteristics of patients with Meniere's disease compared with patients with vertigo, tinnitus or hearing loss. ENT journal, 148-156, 2007

Savastano M, Maron MB, Mangialaio M, Longhi P, Rizzardo R. Illness behavior, personality traits, anxiety and depression in patients with Meniere's disease. J Otolaryngol 1996 Oct;25(5):329-333.

Sato G1, Sekine K, Matsuda K, Ueeda H, Horii A, Nishiike S, Kitahara T, Uno A, Imai T, Inohara H, Takeda N. Long-term prognosis of hearing loss in patients with unilateral Ménière's disease. Acta Otolaryngol. 2014 Jul 16:1-6. [Epub]

Soto-Varela A1, Huertas-Pardo B, Gayoso-Diz P, Santos-Perez S, Sanchez-Sellero I. Disability perception in Ménière's disease: when, how much and why? Eur Arch Otorhinolaryngol. 2015 May

1. [Epub]

Stahle J, Friberg U, Svedberg A. Long-term progression of Meniere's disease. Acta Otolaryngol (Stockh) 1991:Suppl 485:75-83

Thirlwall, A. S. and S. Kundu (2006). 'Diuretics for Meniere's disease or syndrome.' Cochrane Database Syst Rev 3: CD003599.

'Ménière's Disease.' The Alternate Advisor: The Complete Guide to Natural Therapies and Alternative Treatments. Edited by Robert. Richmond, VA: Time-Life Books, 1997

Meniere Networks

Meniere's Society (UNITED KINGDOM)
www. menieres.org.uk

Meniere's Society Australia
(AUSTRALIA)info@menieres.org.au

The Meniere's Resource & Information Centre
(AUSTRALIA) www.menieres.org.au

Healthy Hearing & Balance Care (AUSTRALIA)
www.healthyhearing.com.au

Vestibular Disorders Association (AUSTRALIA)
www.vestibular .org

The Dizziness and Balance Disorders Centre
(AUSTRALIA)
www.dizzinessbalancedisorders.com

Meniere's Research Fund Inc (AUSTRALIA)
www.menieresresearch.org.au

Australian Psychological Society APS
(AUSTRALIA) www.psychology.org.au

Meniere's Disease Information Center (USA)
www.menieresinfo.com

Vestibular Disorders Association (USA)
www.vestibular.org

WebMD.
www.webmd.com

National Institute for Health
www.medlineplus.gov

Mindful Living Program
www.mindfullivingprograms.com

Center for Mindfulness
www. umassmed.edu.com

Books
Meniere Man
Recommends

Mindful Way Through Depression.
-By Jon Kabat-Zinn

Full Catastrophe Living.
-By Jon Kabat-Zinn

Mindfulness Based Stress Reduction Workbook.
-By Jon Kabat-Zinn

The Man Who Mistook His Wife for a Hat.
-By Oliver Sacks

Stumbling on Happiness.
-By Daniel Todd Gilbert

Still Alice.
-By Lisa Genova

Meniere
Man Mindful
Recovery Series

The books are about how it is possible to go from Meniere sufferer to Meniere survivor. The purpose of this Mindful Recovery Series is a simple one. Each book shares Meniere Man's personal management methods for coping with Meniere's disease, and making a full recovery.

MENIERE'S #1 BEST SELLER 3RD EDITION

MENIERE MAN
MAKE A FULL RECOVERY

MINDFUL RECOVERY

Let's Get Better
MY MENIERE SURVIVOR'S BOOK

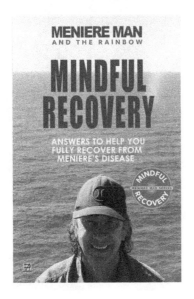

MENIERE MAN
AND THE RAINBOW

MINDFUL RECOVERY
ANSWERS TO HELP YOU
FULLY RECOVER FROM
MENIERE'S DISEASE

MINDFUL RECOVERY

MENIERE MAN
AND THE ASTRONAUT

THE SELF-HELP BOOK FOR MENIERE'S DISEASE

MINDFUL RECOVERY

It's the only positive, yet real account
I've read, of what it's really like.
- L. Forrester.(UK)

MENIERE MAN
AND THE FILM DIRECTOR

THE SELF HELP BOOK FOR MENIERE'S VERTIGO

This book really helped me get up
and get moving. It helped give me the
desire to get on with life.
- CDW

PAGE ADDIE PRESS
UNITED KINGDOM, AUSTRALIA.

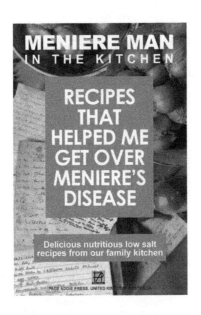

MENIERE MAN
IN THE KITCHEN

RECIPES
THAT
HELPED ME
GET OVER
MENIERE'S
DISEASE

Delicious nutritious low salt
recipes from our family kitchen

PAGE ADDIE PRESS. UNITED KINGDOM. AUSTRALIA

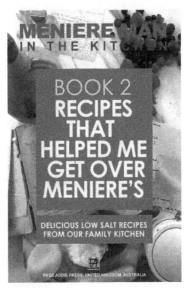

MENIERE MAN
IN THE KITCHEN

BOOK 2
RECIPES
THAT
HELPED ME
GET OVER
MENIERE'S

DELICIOUS LOW SALT RECIPES
FROM OUR FAMILY KITCHEN

PAGE ADDIE PRESS. UNITED KINGDOM. AUSTRALIA

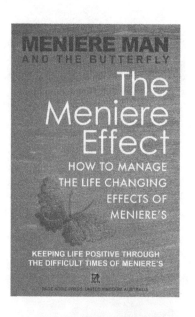

MENIERE MAN
AND THE BUTTERFLY

The
Meniere
Effect

HOW TO MANAGE
THE LIFE CHANGING
EFFECTS OF
MENIERE'S

KEEPING LIFE POSITIVE THROUGH
THE DIFFICULT TIMES OF MENIERE'S

PAGE ADDIE PRESS. UNITED KINGDOM AUSTRALIA

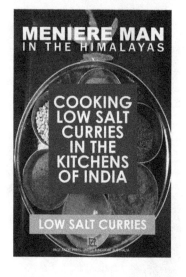

MENIERE MAN
IN THE HIMALAYAS

COOKING
LOW SALT
CURRIES
IN THE
KITCHENS
OF INDIA

LOW SALT CURRIES

PAGE ADDIE PRESS. UNITED KINGDOM AUSTRALIA

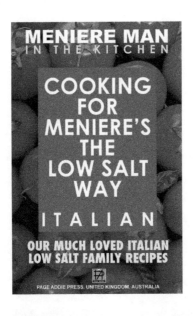

MENIERE MAN
IN THE KITCHEN

COOKING
FOR
MENIERE'S
THE
LOW SALT
WAY

ITALIAN

OUR MUCH LOVED ITALIAN
LOW SALT FAMILY RECIPES

PAGE ADDIE PRESS. UNITED KINGDOM. AUSTRALIA

MENIERE MAN
GUIDED MEDITATION. VOICED BY MENIERE MAN

Let's
Get Better
Relaxing Healing
Meditation

notes

notes

notes

notes